unsafe
at
any
dose

Sales of this book help support the work of
The James Nayler Foundation – www.TruthTrustConsent.com

unsafe at any dose

exposing psychiatric dogmas –

so minds can heal

Dr Bob Johnson

Consultant Psychiatrist   GMC speciality register for psychiatry

formerly   Head of Therapy, Ashworth Maximum Security Hospital, Liverpool

Consultant Psychiatrist, Special Unit, C-Wing, Parkhurst Prison, Isle of Wight

MRCPsych (Member of Royal College of Psychiatrists),
MRCGP (Member of Royal College of General Practitioners).
Diploma in Neurology & Psychiatry (Psychiatric Inst NY),
MA (Psychol), PhD(med computing), MBCS, DPM, MRCS.

☐   ☐   ☐   ☐

Published in 2006 by Trust Consent Publishing,
P O Box 49, Ventnor, Isle of Wight, PO38 9AA UK.
www.TrustConsent.com.

British Library Cataloguing in Publication Data. A CIP record of this book is available on request from the British Library.   ISBN 0-9551985-1-8
ISBN-13 is 978-0-9551985-1-9

10 9 8 7 6 5 4 3 2 1

☐   ☐   ☐   ☐

If you have comments please send them either via the publisher or via www.TruthTrustConsent.com. Sadly, time and age will limit my replies.

**<u>Please note</u> This is a <u>HEALTH WARNING</u>.
Psychiatric drugs are increasingly powerful, they wreak great changes on the chemistry of our brains – so do not stop or change their dosage abruptly, nor attempt to do so without adequate support.**

Sales of this book help support the work of
The James Nayler Foundation – www.TruthTrustConsent.com

☐   ☐   ☐   ☐

Printed by Biddles Ltd, Kings Lynn, Norfolk, PE30 4LS

foreword

"Psychiatric drugs do more harm than good" – not a comfortable statement to read. Your first reaction is likely to be shock, your second, disbelief. After all, doctors have a long and rigorous training – if something was wrong, surely they would be the first to point it out. Sadly, too many doctors share your disbelief. They keep splashing out psychiatric drugs, as if their futures depended on it. For the last 50 years doctors, with few honourable exceptions, have steadfastly ignored the solid, irrefutable evidence that psychiatric drugs prolong disease.

Robert Whitaker's book *Mad In America* gives chapter and verse on the full range of damning scientific evidence. Whitaker himself hoped that by presenting this data, in a calm straightforward manner, matters would improve. Sadly his endeavour has failed. This book is therefore a further effort in the same direction – in effect it says, "Wake up! There's more to psychiatry and to life, than the current psychiatric approach allows."

Unless this psychiatric approach is changed, we are all destined to be treated as mindless unfeeling robots, gummed up by psychiatric drugs. Indeed closer scrutiny shows that today's psychiatric foundations are built on sand, as I reviewed in my earlier book *Emotional Health.* Here I describe what it looks like from the psychiatrist's point of view, and show how a reawakened psychiatry could heal more. We are a sociable species – emotional distress of all varieties is curable. Read it, and see if you agree that public pressure is now urgent.

This is not an anti-psychiatry book. I have been a member of the Royal College of Psychiatrists since 1973. I have studied psychiatry intensively since 1963, and have been a Consultant Psychiatrist since 1991. I love it. Since emotions inflict such terrible agonies, it is imperative that we control them, not them us. Emotion Support Centres – where "recoverers help others recover" – aim to do just that, which is why I now give them my fullest support.

[]   []   []   []

list of chapters

contents

◻   ◻   ◻   ◻

1) WHY IGNORE 50 YEARS OF ADVERSE SCIENTIFIC EVIDENCE?

dogma 1 – ignore the fear

Psychiatry is now a dismal failure. From a strictly medical viewpoint – it doesn't work. Its insistence on a banal mechanistic approach is simplistic and grossly inappropriate. Its obstinate over–reliance on drugs results in epidemics, not cures. Meanwhile, a thick veil of fear hangs over all. Psychiatrists themselves, are often cast in a fearsome light, partly through their association with insanity, which is itself frightening. But also because they repeatedly compel fearfully damaging 'treatments'. Fear impedes rational thought – it's the only thing that does. How can you possibly assess whether psychiatric drugs do more harm than good, if the whole topic comes to you overburdened with forebodings? My advice would be to take the book steadily and calmly. Keep hold of a thread of reason at all times. Make sure you can see some sense in what I write, by relating it to what you are already familiar with. Above all, never stop looking for fear of what you might see – that way madness lies. For my part, I shall endeavour to keep the thread simple, calm and straightforward, relying on the maxim that you should first taste what I write, but swallow only when you see enough sense in it to do so: but when you do, please act.

Insane people are frightening. They are unpredictable and can be dangerous – in fact irrationality is always destructive. My first experience of such dangers occurred in one of my training group therapies in 1963. A man sitting only six chairs away from me, half rose out of his chair, turned and, out of the blue, punched his neighbour hard in the face. All of us were shocked. The man himself, let's call him Jonathon, appeared more shocked than most. I remember him still shuddering at the thought of what he had just done. Once we'd recovered our breath, we asked him what had happened – but he could only mumble incoherently about being 'upset' at the way families were being discussed in the group. He had not participated in the discussion verbally – he communicated his feelings more directly, indeed too directly for comfort.

The psychiatrist running the group at the time had no better idea of what had happened than I. However 30 years later, the 60 murderers I worked closely with in Parkhurst Prison taught me that violence comes from fear. Generally this fear is itself obscured, as it was with Jonathon above. But if you want to unpick an act of violence, look for the fear beneath. In fact, over the last 45 years it has become increasingly obvious to me that emotions play a vital role in all mental disease. And of all the emotions, the one that matters most is fear. In my earlier book, *Emotional Health*, fear is described as the Master Emotion, highlighting the impact it can have, especially when unacknowledged – the so-called buried or obsolete terror.

Fear is the key component in every mental illness. It manifests itself obviously enough in phobias or panic attacks, and in anxieties of all varieties. Paranoia by definition, is fear incarnate; and no psychosis is ever fear-free. Despite this, fear still finds no place in established psychiatry – only dogmatic presumption can keep it out. In real contact with real suffering humanity, it soon becomes obvious that there is a clear analogy between infection in general medicine and fear in psychiatry – unless and until both are detected and controlled, health, physical or mental, is unlikely to be robust.

This is not the first dogma to undermine medical progress – looking back 150 years, we find that bacteria were similarly unacknowledged, and progress was similarly obstructed for many decades. In Victorian times, doctors and especially male midwives actually took pride in not washing their hands when moving from post mortem room to operating theatre. Exposing themselves to soap and water somehow offended their dignity. So they declined – vociferously. There was no evidence they could see, or would look at, which entailed them altering their time-honoured practices – after all, the supposed 'microbes' were entirely and invariably invisible to the naked eye. The very existence of micro-organisms was not readily conceded, and even when it was, their relevance to disease was actively disputed well into the early years of the twentieth century. The absence of recognisable evidence, or at least evidence deemed adequate, allowed the continuation of a pattern of behaviour which today would rightly be regarded as appalling.

It is instructive to look more closely at the circumstances prevailing at the time. Doctors in those days, worked under ferocious pressures. The death rate during operations, especially child-birth, was horrendous, infantile mortality a constant refrain – almost perhaps something to be accepted as an inextricable part of the human condition. So pesky suggestions that they were doing something to make matters worse, attracted spontaneous eruptions of contempt or suppression.

Doctors, especially when pressed, become ever more conservative, one might say dogmatic – what worked before is likely to be less harmful than what is now proposed. Caution becomes the watchword – and unorthodox innovations, especially those suggesting that present remedies do more harm than good, are seen as likely to make matters seriously worse. Accordingly such suggestions are discarded or even crushed with no lack of vigour. After all, viewed through the old orthodoxy – current practice cannot be bettered – it is all there is, else they would have been taught differently in medical school. Sadly today's psychiatric dogmas have long precedents.

denial

Under conditions of fear or stress, rational thought is impaired. How this comes about is actually straightforward enough. The mind has given us our evolutionary advantage by providing us with a mental model of our surroundings. Likely scenarios can be explored in our heads, allowing us to work out a way through our many impending pitfalls, before actually falling prey to them. In particular the mind enables us to construct, and keep in good repair, the social networks which are so essential for our sanity, and indeed our very survival as a species. But this modelling falters if an issue or a subject becomes too painful, or too fearful to contemplate – a flaw which once recognised, can be seen cropping up all over the place.

It is hard enough at the best of times, keeping an up-to-date picture of our ever-changing world in mind – old patterns are constantly being displaced by new, nothing 'out there' is ever static. If stress is added to the mix, life becomes even more difficult. Add overwhelming fear or terror, and rational thought ceases – terror actively induces mental paralysis. Serious discrepancies can then begin to occur between what we think is 'out there' and what actually is. At this point the mind is no longer able to serve its proper function. It can no longer provide reliable guidance as to what to do next. Indeed its overreaction to fear can itself become the main impediment to healthier progress. The mind is ill.

Not only is it helpful to think in terms of the analogy between fear and infection as far as general mental health care is concerned. It is also useful to tease out the correlation between fear and pain, which closely resemble each other. Everyone knows that a painful leg leads first to limping, and can then lead to disuse of the leg entirely. It is common knowledge that pain readily leads to physical immobility, so it is hardly surprising to find that fear does the same for mental agility.

The function of fear is directly parallel to that of pain – both serve to warn us that ignoring them risks further damage. Chest pain is a prime example – 'working through' chest pain is not to be recommended : likewise ignoring a healthy fear of walking across busy motorways is equally life-threatening. Fear becomes toxic however, when the mind is too frightened, and thence too paralysed, to bring itself up to date – earlier threats are perceived as still being operative – unexamined life-saving fears then become life-curtailing.

At its mildest, wilful disregard of present day realities is well recognised as 'wishful thinking' – a conscious preference for what we would like to be the case, when the evidence around indicates otherwise. Unchecked, the next stage along this path is 'day dreaming'. Further down the line, it becomes 'dissociation' – where the mind finds today's reality far too much, so it decides to leave it behind, and move into a world of its own making. The most extreme, of course, is psychosis, where reality is not only abandoned, but re-constructed anew – though even here elements of reality will always tend to seep back, except where drugs dull the appetite to try.

All these mental anomalies fall under the general term 'denial' – in essence, the mind 'denies' what is obvious, and prefers something which appears more benign. So here we have a working definition, a blueprint, for mental illhealth – once the mind no longer relates to the reality around its owner, it is no longer functioning healthily, it is ill. The remedy is also equally clear – supply sufficient quantities of emotional support to allow the mind to cease 'denying', and re-connect itself to current realities. This is the thrust of Emotional Education, of Emotion Support Centres – all aimed at re-gaining control over the emotions. The analogy with a broken leg is sharp – plaster casts support the bones, but the healing is done by the living leg – apply emotional support in an appropriate way, and all minds heal.

Denial is therefore entirely straightforward. A fixed idea already implanted in the mind resists being displaced by a novelty, unless there is adequate reason to do so.

Everywhere in human society, incentives are constantly being proffered to encourage you to change your mind, to change your viewpoint – the advertising industry would not otherwise exist. Equally however, there are a number of disincentives to changing one's mind. The proposed change may appear vague or uncertain; you may be feeling somewhat insecure with what you already 'believe'; it can seem more trouble than it's worth to make the change. I suspect the last partly explains why psychiatry has not yet updated its views on the longer term impact of psychiatric drugs.

Of course as we have seen, there is a whole spectrum of denial, ranging from wishful thinking through day dreams to dissociation even psychosis – and each is accompanied by a similar range in intensity of the disincentive involved. Thus at the milder end, one would expect mild discomfort – "Oh I wish I hadn't missed the bus". More severe would be "I'll wait until all my problems are solved by winning the lottery". Yet more sinister are those pressures we carry over with us from childhood – these can be highly potent, but worse, they are the more actively 'denied' because of that. Childhood traumas can impose the deepest denials. Life support systems in dysfunctional families are not conducive to encouraging the change from infantile dependencies to adult mutual inter-dependencies. These are often the most difficult to remedy. However human beings are nothing if not resilient – given the right support and the appropriate 'education' – change and indeed cure can be expected for all.

dogma 2 – ignore the mind

I want now to try and describe quite what it is like when a medical student is first confronted with mental disease. (Just to be clear, both psychiatrists and psychologists deal with the mind, but only the former, being fully medically qualified, prescribe drugs – so far.) Medical training itself represents the imposition of a whole new way of looking at life, at human beings, indeed at human bodies. This wrench from the norm is accompanied by an entirely foreign vocabulary of some 3000 words which are conspicuously different from everyday usage.

I well remember being confronted with my first abdominal examination. Here in front of me was a torso, the shape and external appearance of which was entirely familiar to me. But such familiarity counted for nothing. Hiding behind the leathery surface were dim, and shifting outlines of vague organs I was called upon to describe immediately in confident detail. Fumbling about with spade shaped hands, I struggled to feel 'the edge of the liver', I delved inexpertly to touch the 'pole of the kidney'. The spleen of course, utterly escaped me. It seemed quite impossible that anyone could make sense of the slightest twinge, the smallest resistance to the probing fingers in a way that would satisfy the critical questions being demanded. And for the neophyte it was impossible – only long careful training could make sense of the entirely unobvious differences that these oh-so-soft organs made to the enquiring hands. Later of course, I became more skilled – my especial expertise being in palpating colons, but that's another story.

If such difficulties attend the examination of something as tangible as the abdomen and its vital contents, imagine the problems that arise with the mind. First of all you have no fingers to poke this intangible organ. Second, your own mind may have blind spots, resulting from unexamined 'denials' on your part, which render accurate examination difficult if not impossible. Thirdly, the sense of awe which all naïve medical students feel for their superiors – such people can even hear a fourth heart sound – this sense of being in the presence of superior knowledge and skill can seriously distort your precepts.

Though the mind is the most important organ in the body, the 'socialising' organ, it is entirely intangible. There are no external lumps or bumps you can feel to distinguish a healthy organ from its sick counterpart. Despite these problems, which have been known throughout history, it is still curious to observe that established psychiatry 'solves' them by ignoring the mind altogether – giving us dogma 2. The problem is – what you are first taught in medical school, forms the foundation stones for your understanding in later life. If the foundation stones are sound, then so will be your subsequent understanding; if they are faulty, because your first teachers had only a dim view of their topic, your later view is liable to be similarly hampered.

The remedy, as for all items taught in medical school, is to have these basic teachings tried and tested in clinical practice. This entails being open and confident enough to accept clinical axioms that continue to make sense, and to ditch those which fail to improve your patients. It's not always easy. Remember that medical schools hold exams every few months – in these you are required to recite the conventional wisdom of the day. You may disagree, but others have already decided what the correct answers are, since they set the questions in the first place. And they are the ones who fail you, not the other way around. A certain amount of regimentation is inevitable in any medical training – only confident exposure to a wide variety of clinical conditions can rescue this, and indeed save more lives as a result.

By resolutely ignoring the mind, psychiatry today has no alternative but to make psychiatry as inflexible as concrete. This is not so hard to accomplish as it might seem. Indeed it falls in nicely with a profound, persistent, and almost irresistible psychiatric ambition to put the whole troublesome topic on a par with physical medicine – a kind of fallacious psychiatric holy grail, driven by a desperate yearning to make the wonderfully intangible and creative mental organ as concrete as say the liver or the brain.

Humans are forever trying to concretise this most wonderful of all attributes, to regulate it, to make it predictable. There is an entirely regrettable tendency to find, or if need be invent, a clear anatomy of the mind – something comparable to the anatomy of the brain. This leads to enormous difficulties and to much illhealth, as Freud himself exemplifies.

Sigmund Freud was perhaps the sharpest clinical observer of his day. Unhappily he was an indifferent philosopher (though vastly superior in this regard when compared to those currently commanding our psychiatric heights, as the next chapter explores). He started out life as a neurologist, where the superficial anatomy of the brain was there for all to see. Then he embarked on an ambitious quest to secure 'The Science of the Mind'. He had no difficulty in dividing the human mind into various parts – he had the greatest difficulty in making them stick. For what is obvious to one mind, is obscure to another; what sounds like an instinct, a complex, an ego to one, is mere tittle-tattle to another – and there is no solid, reliable, objective way of deciding the issue between them. Nor ever will be.

despair

Freud for all his flaws, and they were considerable, had two great contributions to make to our understanding of the human mind. Firstly he took a stand against dogma 2 – he asserted that the mind existed, he asserted 'psychic reality', he proceeded on the basis that there was something called the mind, that it was of crucial importance, and that the primary way to access it was to talk to it. This may count as small beer to non-psychiatrists – but I recently read through 10 years of the British Journal of Psychiatry, and found only two mentions of 'mind': one was decidedly shame-faced and tentative, and the other was by that professional amateur, the Prince of Wales. So Freud is to be applauded for saying we each have a mind that demands respect and fully deserves to be talked to.

The second asset he provided was to insist that part of the mind was not immediately accessible. He made a series of painful, costly blunders as to what to do about that, but the notion that the individual in front of you is not disclosing the key emotional fact in his or her case is crucial to any successful progress in psychiatry. This falls under the heading 'denial' as described above, though that is not quite how Freud himself would have expressed it. And it arises from fear, which Freud ignored as heartily as any modern psychiatrist, and for much the same reasons (see *Emotional Health*).

The impact of this last point, of denial, is unusually profound. Elsewhere in general medicine, the clinical process relies on the individual patient describing the symptoms, relating them to past circumstances, and generally telling the truth about their disease. Indeed the most valuable clinical aphorism I took with me from medical school was Sir William Osler's – "Listen to the patient s/he is telling you the diagnosis". Since the key pathology in psychiatry is denial, then this is no longer the case. Indeed the patient is determinedly keeping from you, and from themselves, the key emotional fact without which progress is impossible. It is simply too painful for them – all they can do is 'deny' it. While this certainly adds to the apparent complexity of psychiatry – once mastered, it is tremendously exciting and fruitful to watch human minds blossom out of their frozen pasts.

Sadly psychiatry reacted adversely to Freud – his flaws were too extensive, his 'anatomy' too rigid and too singular, and even his method of treatment too inflexible and longwinded. Accordingly Freud proved a false god. The rigidity, precision and reproducibility that this branch of the medical profession so craves, which Freud appeared initially to offer, has never materialised, and there are sound philosophical even logical grounds to indicate it never will. The human mind is the most creative, delightful, fluid and inventive entity in the entire cosmos – it does not take kindly to regimentation, dissection, anatomisation or any of the other false structures which a beleaguered profession might wish to inflict upon it. The psychiatric holy grail for which so many yearn must in reality, be exorcised. There are alternative strategies which being more realistic are also more successful – but they can never see the light of day, while this addiction to concretism, this dogma 2, holds sway.

What psychiatry has failed to find in reality, it has decided to invent and impose. The problem is that any structure you invent is the categoric opposite of what the mind actually is. Rigidities, inflexibilities, lack of creativity or consent may make for a fine wish list – but as these characteristics grow, their relevance to the entity they are trying to represent, shrinks.

Given the collapse of Freud, given the intense desire, nay need, to be as physical and organic as general medicine – the outcome has been despair. A deep psychiatric nihilism has descended on the profession I love. A whole catalogue of daffy diagnoses has been compiled as a bulwark against a protean, amorphous and constantly changing psychic scene – I review it later. The mind delights in picking holes in arguments, in creating exceptions to rules and regimentations – sadly the current psychiatric insistence that mental disease is essentially chemical, genetic or biological is not only counter-intuitive to the non-psychiatrist, it turns out to be doubly flawed. It is wrong on two counts. Firstly there is solid evidence that this approach is failing globally – Robert Whitaker, who will be mentioned frequently anon, counts the number of mentally disabled as growing by 400 a day – a number that should be shrinking, if the current psychiatric foundations were realistic. And secondly, the drugs which are currently thrust into the widening gap between agonising mental symptoms, and out-of-touch psychiatrists' rigidities, have themselves proved pathogenic – thus the crutch built of mind-altering chemicals has not only buckled under the weight of reliance that psychiatry feels increasingly obliged to place upon it, but has proved corrosive in the process.

In short, psychiatry today prescribes damaging drugs because it despairs of anything better. Unhappily the ever increasing evidence that these drugs inflict damage coincides with a parallel increase in the pressures under which psychiatry currently finds itself, leaving ever less room for rational evaluation of the growing scientifically proven evidence that these drugs do far more harm than good.

This book is intended to awaken wider interest in and understanding of this dilemma, so that more humane, more secure and more successful psychiatric approaches can prevail. Any drug that alters the mind is grasped with both hands – why bother with a chemical that is psychically inert. However, given that chemically altered minds think and talk less well, and given that talking is the main gateway to the mind – all mind altering drugs must inevitably be unsafe at any dose.

drunk

It is of the greatest importance that a clear understandable thread runs through this book, one that is obvious to all. Without relating what I write to what makes sense to you, then not only am I breaching the maxim offered in the first paragraph of the book, but I will soon be writing for dwindling numbers. So we need to be a little canny when approaching the question of what current psychiatric drugs actually do.

Let's make one thing clear – no one knows exactly what psychiatric drugs do. There are countless models, theories and chemical interactions which are put forward, and frequently clung to for want of something better. But precise knowledge of how drugs impact on brain tissue, is puny. Enormous moment is attached to increasingly detailed scans of the brain – PET scans, MRI scans, fMRI and many others – and indeed much more data is now available than ever before. But what it all shows is that there is vastly more to know. Scratching the surface is not really an appropriate description – tinkering with the gravel in the drive-way is rather more like it. Parts of the brain are more concerned with some things than with others, why should this surprise us? For example, when emotions are discussed, you are likely to hear "Ah yes, it's the limbic system". This is about as much practical use as saying – "Tsunamis. Ah yes, it's the salt water".

Though it is certainly true that no one knows exactly what psychiatric drugs actually do, indeed how they actually work – one thing all agree on is that they impact on the mind, else why use them in the first place. Further if the mind heals itself on being given appropriate support, just as a leg bone will – then any chemical which impinges on it, runs the serious risk of deferring or indeed defeating such healing – a point consistently confirmed by objective, repeatable scientific evidence over the last 50 years.

The holy grail for which all concrete psychiatry yearns is a fixed anatomy as just described – alias dogma 2. This illusion is kept alive by regurgitating gobbets of data every so often, which link ever smaller parts of the brain with ever more complex and ever less well defined human behaviour patterns. The grail is made to appear just that bit less out of reach by the supposition that there is a gene, a location, a micro-neurological niche which mirrors the oh-so-slippery psychiatric symptom in question.

What is overlooked is the infinite complexity of the mind. The brain may appear complicated – but what it supports in the way of mental activity is infinitely more so. And infinity, on the school boy's definition is the biggest number you can think of, plus one – and having now thought of this new number, you have to add one more, and so on, endlessly. This is exactly what our delving into micro-neurology repeats, ad infinitum. Each new datum pulls further mysteries out of the cerebral porridge, like an unbreakable string of unknowable sausages, which serve only to reveal ever greater ignorances. But however complicated neural processes are found to be, it is as well to recall that those of the mind are invariably more so – indeed there is ample reason to suppose we will never fully comprehend the human mind – but then we don't need to. All we need to know is how to heal it, an outcome contemporary psychiatry seems to become ever less familiar with.

And all the time, this pursuit of microscopic brain function, this headlong advance is in the wrong direction – therefore it must inevitably and increasingly ignore the best channel into the human mind, which as Freud averred, is to talk to it. The point is readily shown by asking the simple question as to whether the individual under the scan is thinking in English or in Chinese. It matters a great deal to them and to us, and is immediately decided upon opening our mouths – a conclusion no amount of scanning can ever reach.

The brain on which these drugs have impact is infinitely complex. Not only is it infinitely complex, but it will invariably and for ever remain so. So to imagine that there is a simple explanation for what a given drug actually does, is, well, imaginary. The substrate, or point of impact of the drug, is already rather more complex than we can ever conceive, so we have no need here, to strain comprehension by attempting to describe it. I have no objection to learning more about which enzyme system in the brain is altered by which drug – I have a powerful objection to the suggestion that this is all we need to know, or that it is somehow relevant to pressing irrationalities, anxieties, denials or depressions. The implication is that drugs are more important than talk, that drugs hold out remedies for the multitude of mental afflictions from which so many suffer. Now that I object to as strenuously as possible – in my view, it's myopic tosh.

Despite this inherent complexity, indeed because of it, we need some sort of practical handle on what mind altering drugs are like. How do they operate in general, and what harm do they cause? Practical experience is again essential to maintain that sturdy thread of sense throughout this discussion. In view of the complexities which await us, as bottomless pits open on every hand, let's start with the most widely used mind-altering substance of them all – alcohol. This is a chemical with which everyone is familiar, some perhaps too much so. By examining its features more closely, we can gain a clearer understanding of what psychiatric drugs are about.

The Bible commends alcohol on the grounds that it "maketh glad the heart of man" – sadly that wise tome fails to add that alcohol also "rotteth the liver something chronic." In some quarters it is highly spoken of as giving "Dutch Courage", i.e. a type of false bravery which would otherwise not be available. And it can be little doubted that alcohol is the most used tranquiliser, bar none. A stressful event is followed more frequently by "I need a drink" than by anything else.

The notion of Dutch Courage is an important one. Calling it by that name is merely for communicative expedience – no disrespect is intended to our Netherlander cousins. In fact, it would be historically more accurate to label it British Courage, as I imagine it may well be on other shores. The reason being that when the Romans invaded us in 55 BC, all their battles were fought on a strictly abstemious basis. Alcohol was freely available, but never to troops going into battle – that was reserved to the Ancient Britains who regularly boosted their failing courage by resort to the bottle, thereby proving even less of a match for their formidably proficient opponents.

The actions of alcohol on the human mind need little description. There is generally an initial euphoria. This is rapidly followed by confusion or befuddlement. Cell damage has long been associated with exposure to alcohol, especially in the liver, but also in the brain. Excessive doses lead inevitably first to coma, thence death. Alcohol is peculiarly effective at preserving tissue samples, and other biological products – hence its use as a preservative in pickled pathology specimens. Obviously the same pickling occurs in everyone who drinks it – more in heavier doses, less in smaller ones.

In the longer term, the effects of the same dose become attenuated, so more has to be consumed to induce the same impact – in effect the body deploys enzymes to remove the toxin, and grows more of these as the demand arises. Habituation occurs, leading to more being needed to achieve the same outcome. Used as a sedative, this can lead to addiction – for though with repeated use the euphoria is briefer – cell death remains dose related.

Of course what alcohol is doing, as the Romans' opponents used it for, is to reduce fear. And this is generally how psychiatric drugs work today. There are better ways of reducing fear which avoid such obvious chemical risks. But it is surprising how scientific evidence is accumulating that each group of psychiatric drugs, though varying in some points, nevertheless mimics alcohol in providing initial welcome sedation, while in the longer term inflicting cell damage, addiction and generally prolonging the symptoms which brought the patient to the doctor in the first place. Thus it is not too far fetched to suggest that psychiatric drugs work by making the patient in a manner of speaking, drunk. This is perhaps how they produce their initial benefit – they reduce, briefly, the fears which gave rise to the psychiatric symptoms in the first place.

Viewed in this light, it is easy to see how psychiatric drugs interfere with rational thought – for without impact on the mind at all, they hold no psychiatric interest. But since the mind is the organ of socialising, individuals who are drugged become socially uninteresting, they interact less socially. This is so blindingly obvious with alcohol – it should come as no surprise that it applies to all psychiatric drugs. And since supported socialising is the remedy for emotional distress – all psychiatric drugs are unsafe, whatever their dose.

short term benefit – long term disaster

The major tranquilisers were first studied scientifically in the late 1950s, in the so-called Nine Hospital Study. Patients were divided into four groups – three given the new psychiatric drugs, the fourth group a placebo to act as control. After six weeks, the drugged group were materially better – fewer hallucinations, fewer psychotic symptoms in general. However, after 12 months, the reverse was the case – the drugged group had a higher relapse rate than the placebo group, a rate which was directly proportional to the quantity of drug consumed.

Obviously such a disturbing finding needed repeating – yet every time the question is investigated scientifically, the result is always the same – those given drugs do worse than those not. In the late 1960s for example, a World Health Organisation study found that those falling ill in developing countries where psychiatric drugs are too expensive, fared vastly better and went back to work far quicker than those falling ill in the West, where psychiatric drugs are prescribed as being as close to soul-saving as a concretist profession can allow itself.

What these studies repeatedly show is that drugs given by psychiatrists actually prolong the disease for which they are given. The patients would be better off if they received no psychiatric drug treatment – they would get better sooner, and for longer – a dramatic result that has been repeated with the same outcome every time. Robert Whitaker, author of *Mad in America*, from which this account is taken, concludes that the psychiatric profession on seeing the benign results at six weeks, whooped with joy at making some impression on the psychiatric nihilisms of the time, and could not be persuaded to look any further, certainly not at the data from 12 months on. Had they done so, the early benefits would be gone.

Some blame pharmaceutical companies for producing and marketing these psychiatric drugs so effectively. And there is certainly no doubt that market forces have a perverse impact on health generally – the USA for example, spends vastly more on health care, while leaving vastly more of its citizens without. However no doctor alive would now prescribe thalidomide during pregnancy – and a similar revulsion will apply to psychiatric drugs once their detrimental impact registers. It is one thing to call for drug induced sedation as a temporary measure while remaining fully aware of the dangers involved in doing so, as many now call for alcohol – but quite another to insist that psychiatric drugs are equivalent to giving insulin to diabetics, which represents psychiatric dogma gone dangerously and toxically mad. Insulin after all does not inflict brain cell death – psychiatric drugs do.

dogma 3 – ignore the software

The bulk of this first chapter has been to explore how the current psychiatric drug anomaly could possibly have come about. For the question is no longer "Is it scientifically proven that psychiatric drugs do more harm than good?", but "Why are they still prescribed, and in ever increasing quantities?". How can a group of dedicated and well-trained men and women persist in prescribing drugs which have been repeatedly and scientifically shown to prolong the disease they are intended to treat?

Were doubts about these drugs ever to be hinted at, then surely the psychiatric profession would be the first to blow the whistle. To the non-psychiatrist, it must seem inconceivable that a branch of the august medical profession would actively participate in a cover-up of mammoth proportions, and to persist in this for fully half a century. If it were once demonstrated that those receiving anti-psychotic drugs for example, suffered higher relapse rates than those not – then the first thing a responsible profession would do is review the whole process, re-examine all the basic issues involved, and start over with a clean sheet. With evidence as stark as I describe, what possible reason could induce such a large body of intelligent and highly trained men and women to ignore it?

The evidence in question is expounded further in later chapters – the foregoing is offered as a pathway to guide the reader to think the matter through and come to their own conclusions. Again, the maxim with which the book opened still holds – taste what is offered, swallow only when satisfied it makes sense – but when it does, act.

As this chapter closes, it might help to review the dogmas which contemporary psychiatry ferociously adheres to. These help explain, at least to me, how this massive iatrogenic disaster came about and why it persists so powerfully today. Whitaker, a sober man if ever I met one, calls it an epidemic [see his paper in the Appendix].

Thus the first dogma – ignoring the fear – arises inevitably from the current insistence on concrete models of the mind. This has the unhealthy consequence of reducing the significance of emotions to a psychiatric footnote. By displacing fear from its central clinical role, it becomes impossible to evaluate how fear impedes thought. Which is a pity, since this is the main pathology in mental disease – indeed recognising denial is the first step to mental wellness, both for the psychiatrist or other therapist or emotional supporter, and for the sufferer themselves, who can then be persuaded that there is life after confronting this 'worst possible fear in all the world'.

The second dogma, ignoring the mind, arises because this most important of all human organs is, by its very nature intangible. It cannot possibly be otherwise, else it would lose its key asset. The floorboard we evaluate in our minds before risking it with our body weight, has no substance whatsoever; the falling off the cliff which we can so clearly envisage, hasn't happened in any physical reality; the 'living happily ever after' has explicitly not yet materialised. In all such cases, if our mental furniture were concrete, then the creativity, the thinking things through, the chance to find a different pathway – all these would be unavailable. The mind is intangible, it maintains a symbolic world – the symbols are fluid and flexible – where they are not, health, indeed very survival is imperilled.

If the first two dogmas are not effectively expunged, then the third remains obscured. Failing to appreciate the full part emotions play, especially fear, coupled with distorting the true nature of the mind itself, by succumbing to an overwhelming yearning for a concrete model – both these nullify the fact that psychiatric problems arise from software not hardware. Dogma 3 leads to a regrettable ignoring of the software element in psychiatric practice. This in itself multiplies the risk of iatrogenic disease enormously.

Anyone with experience of computers soon learns that when they malfunction, the most likely cause is software error. Computers after all, have had some 50 years of intense evolution and development, so the hardware is now mostly solid state, with failure rates in the billions, even trillions of cycles. It is scarcely worth opening the box of these new machines to see what is wrong, since it's all solid sate in there, and where it's not, the engineering tolerances are down to millionths of a metre or less.

The human brain has been evolving for around a million times longer – the hardware here rarely goes awry – why should it? Indeed why on earth should it? To do so on a scale the current psychiatric approach requires, flies in the face of all clinical expectation. An epidemic of brain disease? – where's the extensive neurological damage? Vastly more likely is that the individual has been 'mis-programmed', by association with traumatic or fearful earlier experiences. You don't have to be an expert to understand that fear interferes with rational thought – in fact, professional psychiatric training is all too likely to prevent such a notion entering your mind in the first place.

2) WHAT EXACTLY ARE YOU TREATING?

medical realities

My medical friend could scarcely believe his ears – he looked at me closely the way you scrutinise someone who offers to demonstrate levitation. I repeated that schizophrenia was an episodic disease – it came and went, depending on circumstances. "No," he said. "I have always been taught that it is a permanent condition – once diagnosed you have it for life." I could tell that he was struggling between finally dismissing me as an out-of-touch crank, whom it would be best to humour – or with stretching his mind to accommodate an astonishing fact which blatantly contravened all he had been taught on the matter. As if to clinch the point, he said, "My psychiatric lecturer assured us that if she woke up one morning hearing voices, she would kill herself – on the assumption that the diagnosis of psychosis is intractable and permanent."

Now here was a thoughtful doctor, a man obviously competent in his job (which was not psychiatric), with a keen medical curiosity – and yet the notion that schizophrenia, or psychosis was a disease capable of 100% cure, was something he would immediately have dismissed out of hand had our personal relationship been less strong. I have known him for a number of years, and his wife for 30. It is easy to see, especially taking into account the points raised in the previous chapter, that the current psychiatric prejudice about the permanence of schizophrenia will be hard to shift. Medical evidence has a way of being finessed into oblivion when the basis of one's knowledge is being tweaked, or in this case thrown out of the window.

What's the evidence that convinced me? I began my psychiatric career on 1st January 1963, at Claybury Hospital on the outskirts of London. I could not have had a better start – Dr Denis Martin the then Superintendent was a wonderfully tolerant charismatic man, a positive inspiration. It was the heyday of that humane psychiatric approach – The Therapeutic Community – everyone was involved in helping the sick recover, even the ward cleaner sat in on the ward group meetings in the mornings, contributing to the benign social reality in the ward. This was the 'Healing Hand of Kindness' writ large, and an inspiring and educative process it was.

Claybury was one of 15 or so large Victorian Lunatic Asylums built like a necklace around London, to accommodate the growing number of nineteenth century psychotic patients. It had one or two acute wards, where I spent most of my time, and a larger number of 'back wards' where the chronic and 'incurables' were lodged. Every so often, one of the latter would require a medical report for life insurance or similar purposes. It fell to me to answer a number of questions about their health. The routine was straightforward enough – you looked through the elderly medical records – wonderful documents at least A3 (16 x 12 inches) in size, if not bigger – and as soon as you found the rubber stamp imprint 'SCHIZOPHRENIC', you stopped looking, ticked the box on the form, and posted it off. That was how it was done then.

In 1967 my first psychiatric career came to an abrupt end. I was happy in my work, had done original research on Freud's treatment of obsessional neuroses, and was running a unit with far more clinical responsibility than my then rank normally allowed. Since I regarded Electro Convulsive Treatment (ECT) as barbaric (and still do), I guided all my patients away from it. Unhappily this incurred my consultant's displeasure who reacted by blacklisting my psychiatric career. Thus later that same year, I found myself working in general practice. After an initial adjustment, it was there that I learnt what real psychiatry is.

I had not been working long in my new setting before a man presented himself with clear psychotic symptoms – the walls were talking to him, so he received the automatic rubber stamp 'SCHIZOPHRENIA'. I packed him off with Stelazine, followed him up, and thought no more about it. Some 18 months later he attended again. "Ah", said I, confidently, "what about the voices?". "Voices?", he replied, "What voices? I haven't had any voices for ages. No, I've come about my back-pain – it's killing me".

I was 30 at the time, immensely keen to unpack the mysteries of psychiatry that had eluded Freud, so I took this as serious clinical evidence, which it manifestly was. It occurred to me that I had been taught in a teaching hospital. I had not been taught in general practice. Hospital doctors see patients referred to hospital – they do not generally see them when they are well, and functioning healthily in the community, something general practitioners do everyday. It follows that florid cases of psychosis are commonplace in hospital – but when they remit, they no longer need to attend, so fail to educate the doctors there, to the true nature of the disease.

Precisely the same applied to osteo-arthritis of the knee. I was confidently assured in my medical school teaching hospital that this disease afflicted the hip, but never the knee. This was at the time the first hip operations were being performed in key hospitals – knee replacements were still in the future, and so failed to appear in large central London hospitals, whence this inaccurate medical dogma arose. Had I contradicted it, I would have failed my exams.

Thus on arrival in general practice, I was presented with a woman with a painful, red, swollen knee. "My heavens," I thought, "this must be a rare infection, since arthritis of the knee does not occur". My senior partner, whom I naturally urgently consulted on the point, was not gentle in assuring me that this was indeed arthritis of the knee. He deployed a tone of voice entirely appropriate to dressing down a miscreant school boy – ah, the drawbacks of a deficient medical education.

In discussing these medical prejudices with Robert Whitaker, whose work was a substantial inspiration for this book, he pointed out that it had first arisen with Kraepelin in 1899, with his concept of Dementia Praecox, or premature madness. I surmised that most of his cases at that time were likely to have been syphilitic, which gives rise in Tertiary Syphilis to the well known General Paralysis of the Insane. This latter type of insanity, once established, is unquestionably permanent, with permanent brain damage at its core. Perhaps this notion of permanence then spread to all mental disorders. Though why it manages to persist against decades of sound clinical evidence is quite astonishing – some of the possible factors involved were addressed in the last chapter. Its implications for today's psychiatric practice are profound.

The question is not trivial – it goes to the very heart of psychiatric practice, and indeed to the use or abuse of psychiatric drugs. If you are convinced that the person in front of you has permanent mental disease, for which there is never to be any cure, then for one thing you are going to offer no hope, and for another if drugs have side-effects, their use can be fully justified by the intractability of the disease.

Of course, were the drugs to become the main agent for prolonging that disease, this might be harder to swallow, though generally it is likely to be far too painful a notion to contemplate comfortably for long. But either way, before you reach this grim conclusion, it behoves you to find out if the basis for your pessimism is true – can psychoses be cured – have you an accurate grasp of psychiatric reality? Or is this some sort of professional daydream, or Heaven forbid, denial?

psychiatric nihilism

The general reader may begin to wonder at the scale of psychiatric disarray, the vista of so many dire disasters in the current psychiatric approach would surely shake the most robust constitution. Indeed the damage done by psychiatric drugs needs to be set alongside the gaping holes in psychiatric 'understanding' which are equally damaging, if not more so – and we've hardly started our review. Accordingly, the need for that thread of meaningfulness in a disturbingly topsy-turvy world, becomes ever greater. So setting the above into an everyday context, we can return to our painful leg.

Suppose the doctor treating you, were to say – "Your leg is broken. This is a life long condition – so keep the plaster cast on for the rest of your life." "Just a minute," you might say, "is there no evidence of legs healing?" To which the doctor replies that she's heard mention of some, but it's largely anecdotal, and rather than run the very serious risk of raising false hopes, she insists you do as she says. Moreover, should you demur, she is duty bound to invoke legal compulsion to compel you, legal powers governments shamefully hasten to augment. Thus, when the plaster comes off, a year or two later, your leg is so weak, it cannot support you – "see what I mean", comes the medical rejoinder.

I am struggling to keep that thread calm, which was my part of the bargain in the initial maxim. But it beggars belief that on this most fundamental of all points, psychiatry today keeps itself, its patients and its students, grotesquely misinformed. Suppose you accept the case that powerful mind-altering drugs impose chemical penalties – surely it is desperately important to discover what the so-called natural history of the disease actually is. That is to say, is it or is it not the case that psychotic patients recover 100%? Clearly more is at stake here than the life and possible suicide of an grotesquely misinformed psychiatric lecturer. And understandably enough, the issue has been explored, scrutinised, evaluated and aired many times over. Double blind trials have come and gone – yet this fundamental psychiatric dogma remains entirely unmoved.

One corollary of the drug trials mentioned in the last chapter, and described extensively by Robert Whitaker, is that those in the control groups, i.e. those not receiving psychiatric drugs, got better. They went back to work, they picked up their lives and continued on, very much as if they no longer suffered from psychosis. So the objective, scientific, fully controlled, double-blind evidence is abundant – but just as thoroughly finessed. Psychiatry appears to have other fish to fry, and declines to include this astonishingly obvious fact in its body of knowledge. Those not complying with this exclusion are designated as being beyond the pale and dismissed as dangerous mavericks – thereby disposing of a challenging issue for yet another generation.

One of the more unpleasant side-effects of the psychiatric neglect of the mind, described in the previous chapter as dogma 2, is a serious disrespect for that organ. This leads to the patient as witness, being seriously degraded. The evidence given by sufferers from mental distress is explicitly taken with a pinch of salt, if taken at all. So when the latter maintain that they are now fully healthy, their assertion is side-lined – after all, once mentally ill, always liable to delusions. Equally when they complain of gross drug-induced side-effects – who's to say that these are not really further manifestations of their original disease. So when the Nine Hospital Study of 50 years ago indicates that the prescribing of psychiatric drugs prolongs the disease, a handy medical riposte is to assert that the disease was of the prolonged variety in the first place – thereby exonerating medical input, and relieving psychiatrists of having to re-think any of their fundamentals.

Alice in Wonderland had an easier time of it. The same predisposing factors which lead psychiatrists to discount the possibility of cure of the psychoses, extend now almost as a matter of course to the so-called Personality Disorders. Another digression into my medical student days might assist. As I recently explained to an unimpressed judge, the patter we used to clarify the classification of mental disease was as follows – "Neurotics build castles in the air, psychotics live in them, and psychiatrists draw the rent." In our then robust view, the group of patients that doctors failed to either diagnose or treat had the label 'psychopath' pinned on them – more for the doctor's benefit than otherwise.

With the gradual ossification of the psychiatric profession over the last half-century, these terms, and indeed the simple, handy, flexible classification that goes with them, has lost favour. Nowadays neurosis has transmogrified into Personality Disorder, psychosis into Mental Illness, and psychopath into 'Dangerous Severe Personality Disorder'. In my time, neurosis was considered by far the more favourable diagnosis – now the label Personality Disorder hangs round the neck even more indelibly than psychosis. It's hard to fathom, but somehow because there has never been a pill to treat Personality Disorders, then by an unconscionable sleight of hand, they are edged out of the psychiatric arena. Personality then becomes something you are born with, and therefore not something that medical science can or indeed should tamper with. The fact that emotional distress entails enormous suffering, indeed agony, fades. Not for the first time, the psychiatric view of reality takes precedence over painful hard-edged humanity – with unhappy, and unhealthy consequences on every side.

daffy diagnoses

Not long ago, those who criticised The Bible could expect to burn. An entirely analogous fate awaits those who propose to tamper with the current psychiatric bible the Diagnostic and Statistical Manual of Mental Disorders 4th Edition, 1994 (the DSM–IV). Perhaps by the time this book appears in print we will have been assailed by the 5th edition – sadly all the indications are that it will be just as bizarre as its predecessors.

As I see it, the trouble began with DSM-III in 1980. There has been discussion in the press as to how this came about – how the revision of DSM-II was handed on to a relatively unknown psychiatrist, since it was considered more of a chore than a perk. Whatever its antecedents, the DSM-IV and its immediate successors (including DSM-IV-TR an intermediate edition) accurately reflects the distorted view of psychiatry outlined in the previous chapter. It builds on the three dogmas described there, and thereby raises barriers to the humane, indeed to the safer practice of psychiatry that can seem insurmountable.

Psychiatric drugs are suspect, the realities of mental illhealth questionable – and now the Classification of Mental Disorders requires urgent dismemberment – small wonder my psychiatric career had its ups and downs. In 1998 I was encouraged by the then editor of The Lancet to air some of these criticisms in his august journal – unhappily what I wrote proved too strong meat for him to publish. The Editor of the British Journal of Psychiatry later protested he had insufficient room for it either, though unlike The Lancet, he responded ill to my suggestion that 500 words would help. As with so many of my collisions with medical colleagues, it appeared far safer to shoot the messenger than listen to a decidedly disconcerting message, a response which alters the material evidence not one jot.

It is important to stress the central role that DSM-IV plays in today's psychiatric practice. It is hard to think of any other branch of medical practice which burdens a single volume with such overweening clinical significance. Every patient in every psychiatric institution is required to be allocated a number from its many pages. It thus controls the way psychiatrists see the psychic pathology that passes daily through their hands. But just as the psychiatric drugs fail to pass close scrutiny, so this unbelievable document crumbles into useless fragments once its tenets and conclusions are exposed to healthier daylight. It is a hard to know which is worse – using drugs which prolong mental disease, or a bible which mangles it out of all human recognition.

The last comment might seem intemperate – but it is based on solid medical evidence. For not only does the DSM-IV seriously distort the structure of the psychiatric knowledge base, which as we have already seen is parlous enough without that – but it traduces orthodox medical practice in a totally unacceptable manner. Unacceptable that is, to all other branches of medical practice, bar none.

It is a sad commentary on the rest of my profession that those dealing with afflictions of the mind are exempted from a scrutiny which scours other branches of medicine making them cleaner and more efficacious than they would otherwise be. Perhaps the standard medical mind just blurs when asked to review matters of the psyche – the intangibility, the lack of concrete facts, and the whole issue of software versus hardware is perhaps too unlike general medical practice to allow the ready application of ordinary acceptable clinical values. Perhaps this lead to The Lancet's otherwise regrettable 1998 decision.

Those readers robust enough to have followed thus far, will welcome a return to that rational thread by which to navigate these swirling, controversial and highly emotively charged issues. Take the medical example we've used before – the painful leg. Now there are two central criticisms of the DSM-IV – causative factors, and classification criteria. And this is how the first would apply to leg pain.

As before, your doctor says – "You've got a broken leg. I'm not the least interested in finding out what led up to this. In fact we have recently adopted a significantly novel approach – we've decided to be entirely neutral as to whichever causative factor might have led to this break." "But," you say, "it happened when I fell down." "Ah," comes the reply. "You shouldn't believe all you read. Lots of people fall down. If that was the cause of broken legs – we'd be inundated – so that's not material. The established view therefore is that a connection between falls and fractures is unlikely, to say the least. Either way, it will have no impact on my medical treatment of your current condition."

Now this is manifestly absurd. A doctor talking in this way, indeed any doctor anywhere stating explicitly they had not the least interest in finding out where a disease came from, what its causative factors were, would be reprimanded at the least, and barred from practice at best. The cloud of causative factors which precede any disease is referred to medically as its 'aetiology', or in the USA, its 'etiology'. In philosophical terms, this is the pragmatic clinical response to Hume's Critique of Causality, and a remarkably effective one it generally is. Except here.

Sceptics might find it hard to believe that our current psychiatric bible advocates disregarding all causative factors, all considerations of aetiology. But those interested in a healthier psychiatry will find the following in its opening pages. Being *"neutral with respect to theories of etiology"* is an *"important methodological innovation."* If that's not clear enough, try – *". . . a diagnosis does not carry any necessary implications regarding the causes of the individual's mental disorder. . . Inclusion of a disorder . . does not require that there be knowledge about its etiology."* Indeed, whereas DSM-I, the first edition of all the DSMs, published in 1952, *"reflected Adolf Meyer's . . . view that mental disorders represented reactions of the personality to psychological, social and biological factors"*, which seems eminently practicable, later editions deliberately *"eliminated the term reaction."* [Detailed references are given in the 1998 article reprinted in the Appendix of this book].

Wow. Is this unbelievable? For 26 years this has been the gospel according to the American Psychiatric Association. Thus every medical student pursuing psychiatry will be taught from its pages, every candidate for higher psychiatric qualifications will be required to regard this as an unimpeachable reference source. Amend it at your peril – at peril of your career that is. Thus any who advocate fundamental reform, which is what this book represents, are written out of the script, are safely sidelined as being out-of-date, or out-of-touch – certainly they are out-of-the-loop. This book represents an attempt to widen that loop. And in particular to widen it to encompass all those currently receiving psychiatric services.

It is perhaps in the nature of professions that they tend to stick together; Adam Smith, if I recall correctly, had something pertinent to say about them in this respect. Certainly I have found it to be the case with the legal profession. So if things are muddling on in a normally confused and neutral manner, then why attempt to breach the outer palisades, or in my case, struggle to open up the portcullis? But with today's psychiatry, things are not well – Whitaker reports as mentioned, an additional 400 mentally disabled every day – this is the figure in the USA, a comparable figure is likely to be similar for this country. The WHO studies show better psychiatric care in drug-poor countries – pointing to a deeply disturbing problem. Psychiatric drugs are getting stronger every year – reaching ever deeper into our subtle cortical processes. Time surely, to say "unsafe at any dose."

pigeonholing people

Asking a medical student to examine an abdomen for the first time, and pressing them, hard, to decide instantly, whether the liver is unduly enlarged – this has been described in the last chapter. It can be a gruelling experience. Nothing seems the same, nothing seems reliable, everything is woolly, floaty, and indistinct – I shall never forget the leathery, unforgiving feel to the first abdominal wall I ever examined. It's a bit like counting soft peas under a thick rug – with heavy gloves on. But this is easy compared with examining the mind, the one organ in the body which has function without form, physiology without anatomy. So the desperate need to grasp some guidelines, something that is there every time, something you can rely on – this desperation grows with each unsatisfactory, and potentially humiliating, medical contact with this elusive organ.

Others in the medial school start romping away – they have mastered the art of palpating livers, of hearing esoteric heart sounds – their specialities have solid backing in terms of concrete 'signs', scans, x-rays, measurements or indices. Nascent psychiatrists have nothing that remotely comes close. They look at the putatively 'insane', and either see nothing wrong at all; or they start seeing extraordinary features, which are just not apparent to anyone else. The upshot is that the lowest common denominator comes to be applied – hearsay or gossip becomes paramount. Someone declares that this man is schizophrenic, so their records are stamped with enormous relief, as at Claybury, and the indecision, the murk is vanquished – parity with non-psychiatric medicine seems that bit closer.

What DSM-IV does is take this to its ultimate – a whole raft of 'criteria' suddenly become available, a vast array of 'tests' is conjured up – all with the intention of nailing down this embarrassingly mobile, fluid, and apparently shapeless entity, the human mind. This is dogma 2 with a vengeance – this is concretising the most ineffable item in the entire cosmos, skewering the most brilliant source of creativity in the universe, and attempting to encage what by its very essence, is free.

And of course, as with Freud, it fails. Not only does it fail, it falls flat on its face. The assumption is promoted that you can erect a whole 'science' of psychiatry on the falsehood that the mind really is concrete. But this assumption is not without its cost. The practice of medicine in some psychiatric circles falls well below the level of witchcraft, in my direct personal experience. It is simply not feasible to launch a massive endeavour to concretise the mind, and then expect there to be no ill effects.

The DSM-IV serves not only to salve the bruised egos of the academic psychiatrist, but it provides non-psychiatric institutions with an apparent hand-hold on the elusivities of mental distress. Thus insurance companies, governmental agencies, legislators and as we shall shortly see, facile legal brains, are far too delighted with this apparent cornucopia to examine its origins too closely. Such a cornucopia is unprecedented, that is – it has never been there before. The reason being, that in earlier times, gentlemanly conduct, civilised principles, and overall respect for the dignity of the human organism would not have tolerated it. If you are interested in the historical perspective, I see it as yet another infernal aftermath of the First World War which by suffocating and incinerating ideals lead first to logical positivism, linguistic analysis via 'pseudo-scientific behaviourism', thence to DSM-IV psychiatry.

Since no one item of mental furniture is fixed enough to bear the full weight of a universal psychiatric classificatory system, then the obvious alternative is to have a multitude of them. Indeed the more the merrier. In place of my student day's rigmarole about neurotics, psychotics and psychiatrists, which at least has the advantage of being immediately obvious, the DSM-IV comes up with over 400. And we can confidently look forward in DSM-V to exceeding that number, perhaps even reaching the 500 mark – there being nothing to limit the fertile psychiatric imagination. Shouldn't we expect more from psychiatry at the start of our third millennium?

Personality Disorder is the star player in DSM-IV – though quite why this should be so is rather odd, given that the mantra is clear that this is something you are born with, and is therefore even more intractable than old style schizophrenia. There are hundreds of Personality Disorders, each as airily delineated and as copiously supplied with literate detail as its neighbour, and each carrying the deadly plague of indelibility. Given the widespread support for this noxious tome, we can expect yet more in later editions.

Take one of DSM-IV's endeavours to concretise the ineffable - the so-called Histrionic Personality Disorder, selected here because it came most readily to hand. This is defined as *"a pervasive pattern of excessive emotionality and attention seeking beginning by early adulthood and present in a variety of contexts, as indicated by:*

> *(1) Uncomfortable in situations where he is not the centre of attention.*
> *(2) Interaction with others is characterised by inappropriately sexually seductive or provocative behaviour.*
> *(3) Displays rapidly shifting shallow expressions of emotion*
> *(4) Consistently uses physical appearance to draw attention to himself.*
> *(5) Shows self theatricality and exaggerated expressions of emotion.*
> *(6) Considers relationships to be more intimate than they are."*

As if it were a multiple choice exam, you are invited to answer an arbitrary number of these, and if you tick the requisite number of boxes, your final score indicates your success or failure in being awarded the distinction of being able to call yourself a Histrionic Personality Disordered person. But I should warn you – if you gain too many of these 'awards' you can find yourself being incarcerated for life. Pigeonholing human beings is inhuman – to do so under the guise of medical care is unspeakably appalling. And the ill consequences are correspondingly gross.

recipes for unicorn blood

What medical diagnoses should do is guide the medical team to better therapy. At least calling malaria by that name implied it had something to do with 'bad air', which indeed it has, by way of breeding grounds for mosquitoes. Calling a disease a Histrionic Personality Disorder implies it has more to do with theatrical productions than with practical assistance to the mentally suffering. Where's the pathology, where's the lesion, where's the damage that doctors by their very profession are dedicated to limiting if not curing?

Take item one - *(1) Uncomfortable in situations where he is not the centre of attention.* If this is the medical description of a disease, does it imply that by supplying the sufferer with situations in which he gradually learns to enjoy being the centre of attention, this will cause the condition to remit? The fact is that the victim of this disease will never, ever mention that he or she feels 'uncomfortable' in such situations – this is not a symptom that brings the patient to the doctor, demanding treatment. No, this is a symptom dreamt up by doctors to impose on a group of their fellow human beings who happen to be suffering. What on earth is it doing here, when it is obviously doctor-centred and not patient-centred as it should be? Could it be that doctors, DSM-doctors that is, are here more concerned with cataloguing their patients than helping them? Is there are word for that? Is this what we want our doctors to be doing?

The DSM-IV claims to be scientifically based. Those with stout hearts can find the scientific basis in the preamble. There it is scientifically proven that more doctors agree on what is wrong with a given patient using the DSM-IV approach, than otherwise. So here we have proof if proof were needed, that the scientific basis for this unsightly tome is doctor satisfaction, not patient benefit. If you thought I was exaggerating the yearning to be more like general medical practitioners, perhaps this might nudge the matter along for you.

And of course, there is abundant evidence, evidence that does not depend on doctor opinion, that this approach to psychiatric problems doesn't work – the addition of 400 mentally disabled people a day, calls for more focussed action than agreeing the minutiae of mythical diagnostic entities. This is rather worse than counting angels on the heads of pins – real live human beings suffer directly as a result. They are given no hope. They are offered no way through – and we and our governments support the DSM-IV which endorses this. Should we?

I must admit that my endeavour to present a calm description of the way DSM-psychiatrists err, has proved rather more challenging than I can comfortably manage. When I see so much suffering, and hear so much misguided psychiatric advice, it is hard to prevent emotions rising, and tumbling on to the page. My hope is that these emotive protestations do not cloud the issue for the interested reader. Perhaps the wildest accusation that tumbled out in this way is the 'witchcraft' assertion a few paragraphs back. Let me put some flesh on that one. Keep in mind that medical texts are intended to assist doctors to help patients with the symptoms the latter bring to the former. The way the DSM-IV is constructed induces the bizarre and entirely counter-productive situation whereby the doctor suggests to the patient the symptoms he or she thinks the patient displays, and persists in doing so whatever the patient may say to the contrary. This is such a reversal of standard medical practice that it cries out for urgent remedy. Legal remedies are perhaps less available than they should be, as you can see from the following excerpt. This occurred in a legal context, and fully persuaded the legal authorities then present, that the approach was germane, valid, and vastly to be preferred to the one offered by Dr Bob Johnson.

The case before this Tribunal concerned the possible release of a longstanding, and entirely 'burnt-out' patient in a maximum security hospital. The opposing psychiatrist's report proposed Histrionic Personality Disorder as one of several diagnoses, all designed to convince the Tribunal not to release the patient. The report, suitably adjusted, read in part as follows –

> *(1) Uncomfortable in situations where he is not the centre of attention.*

The doctor drew the Tribunal's attention here to an incident when the patient was in the community, prior to the index offence, some 30 years ago.

(2) Interaction with others is characterised by inappropriately sexually seductive or provocative behaviour.

The doctor here describes stories of sexual relationships that have clustered around this individual during his 30 years incarceration.

(3) Displays rapidly shifting shallow expressions of emotion.

While being interviewed, the doctor notes that the patient's emotional states change.

(4) Consistently uses physical appearance to draw attention to himself.

The doctor comments that the patient has drawn attention to his physique on more than one occasion.

(5) Shows self theatricality and exaggerated expressions of emotion.

No comment was made under this rubric.

(6) Considers relationships to be more intimate than they are.

The doctor reports that it is clear that the patient considers relationship to be more intimate than they are.

This kind of gobbledy-gook (toxic gossip my wife calls it) dissuades long term prisoner patients from even applying for legal review of their case. It has also finally dissuaded me from ever participating in such charades again – the damage done to the patient by raising doomed hopes proved more than I could stomach. Further, fully 90% of Tribunals set up to review the diagnosis and risk of long term patients, are persuaded by this sophistry, and comfort themselves by finding against the patient. In Maximum Security Hospitals, namely Broadmoor, Rampton and Ashworth, this figure rises to 99% against. And should you be unfortunate enough to be confined in the last named, whenever a Tribunal recommends your release, in the exceptional 1% of cases, the legal authorities in that institution immediately take the matter to a High Court Judge for legal review, where the matter invariably turns against the patient. Shades of Soviet psychiatry.

It would be a cheap crack to say that this script, and the underlying medical approach, approximate more closely to histrionics than to medicine. But even a brief review of the sort of answers this type of rigid structure encourages must cast doubt on the overall validity of the medical processes involved.

Thus there are inherent contradictions in the items themselves. In item (4) the word *consistently* appears in the rubric, while the 'answer' satisfies itself by saying *on more than one occasion*. Is this adequate? Who is to be the judge in item (6) of how intimate relations may be? Again these are not symptoms – no patient ever describes their emotional distress in these terms. In fact they are putative, concrete 'signs', purporting to be on a par with enlarged livers, and palpable spleens. The psychiatric desire pushing in this direction should by now be obvious – the drastic failure to enhance mental health which accompanies it may also be becoming clearer.

The following should clarify the resemblance to witchcraft. What the doctor does is read in the vast and generally unintelligible book of spells (the DSM-IV), and recite selected phrases – 'Antisocial Personality Disorder', 'psychopathic tendencies', which when mixed with other incantations from legal tomes, such as 'habilitation', 'index offence', 'nature and degree', and other meaningless gibberish, but never 'Winthrop criteria' (which is the legal requirement that any psychiatric condition warranting incarceration must be seen to be *continuing*). These cast a spell over the legal team on the Tribunal, causing them to become purblind to psychiatric misdeeds, while tolerating the most outrageous legal practices, in favour of keeping the 'burnt out' criminal confined to a 'place of treatment' which more resembles a maximum security prison every time I visit.

I was tempted in this chapter to include first hand accounts of this dire impact of DSM-IV, as suffered by those currently detained under its strangulating hold – if this book runs to a second edition, I can include them then, or possibly in a second volume. I will certainly refer to Scott, who asks repeatedly to appear in my 'next book' by name, having been included in my earlier book, *Emotional Health,* by pseudonym. I describe his predicament in the next chapter, since he does indeed demonstrate 'damage in detail'.

The unicorn is a well known mythical beast. In a recent Harry Potter episode it's blood was seen as conferring longevity, if not immortality. My submission here is that it finds its modern representation in the DSM-IV. However the longevity it is hoped to promote is not that of the patients whose mental agonies psychiatry is charged with alleviating. Instead it's that of DSM-psychiatrists desperate above all else, and especially above assisting patients, desperate that is, to establish a science of mental health. It is ironic that while DSM-IV, and DSM-III before it, arose in large part in adverse reaction to Freud, they have succumbed to the same nemesis – turning the ineffable, delightful, creative and ever more surprising human mind into plodding concrete figments, by means of endless baroque myths, or as an earlier paragraph had it, tittle-tattle.

DSM-IV sanctifies the three dogmas

If I were a philosophy professor, that Queen of the Sciences, and if the preamble and introduction to DSM-IV were submitted to me as a high school essay in that discipline, then I would mark it down severely and promptly send it back for a re-write. Should it be returned unimproved, I would fail it out of hand, and insist the writer re-sit the entire course, for clearly their understanding of the most elementary philosophical concepts is woefully inadequate, judged in the most benign light and at the lowest possible academic level.

Sadly the DSM-IV does nothing to ameliorate the three dogmas – indeed it cements them in, as if with reinforced concrete. It may be recalled that dogma 1 was a full-on determination to avoid all consideration of fear. Indeed the whole thrust of this execrable document is to avoid anything as vague and woolly as emotions in general. By relying on an even vaguer notion – that there is a hardware explanation somewhere to be found in the brain – the word 'emotion' simply does not enter the lexicon. Of course it cannot be omitted from the description of the various categories, since patients insist, as patients will, that their symptoms consist exclusively of emotions going wrong.

Thus we find, in the single DSM-IV example plucked out and displayed above, that of the so-called 'Histrionic Personality Disorder', that emotion features robustly in the descriptions. Though I repeat, I cannot find mention, let alone axiomatic justification of it, in the preamble or introduction. Thus in item (1) *Uncomfortable in situations where he is not the centre of attention* – the operative word *'Uncomfortable'* describes the emotions of the individual, indeed how he or she 'feels' – how vague and subjective is that? Much easier for the doctor to step in, take over, and 'prescribe' the feeling for you. That way the doctor ensures she still keeps control of an otherwise dangerously amorphous situation. The cost of doing so of course, is to remove all possible benefit to the patient, a cost too many DSM-psychiatrists seem willing to pay.

Similarly item (3) *Displays rapidly shifting shallow expressions of emotion.* This item explicitly refers to emotion – in this case, *'shallow'* and *'shifting'*. We are to presume that psychiatrists and others operating with this Manual are competent to assess on the spur of the moment quite when an emotion becomes *'shallow'*, and how fast it has to fade before it qualifies for the label *'shifting'*. Not an easy call to make, I would judge, but then all's well when you are concretising the most gloriously flexible and fluid item in the entire cosmos – the human mind.

Item (5) – *Shows self theatricality and exaggerated expressions of emotion* – again we have emotion specifically brought to our attention – though this time on the grounds that there is too much, not too little. A moment's reflection might give rise to the question – how can the same alleged condition, this 'Histrionic

Personality Disorder', how can this present with both too much emotion and also with too little? What is the pathology involved that can present such diametrically opposite quantities of emotion, and yet arise from the same causative factors, and thus justify being included under the same diagnostic label? After a while one begins to tire of pointing out the serial incontinence of this weighty tome – but rest assured, it will not fade easily. How many struggling psychiatric reformers must burn, before its toxic inanity is recognised?

Dogma 2 – ignore the mind – presents the DSM-IV with no difficulty whatever. This dogma is stated quite explicitly. The authors of the DSM-IV make quite clear their intention to do whatever they can to expunge even the very word from their work. Imagine that. A psychiatric text, nay **the** psychiatric bible, and the authors expressly regret they cannot think of any substitute for the word 'mental' in their title (*Diagnostic and Statistical Manual of Mental Disorders*), though not for want of trying.

Why should such a noble calling as the psychiatric speciality take such an aversion to the sole topic of its specialism? Worse, how can it possibly have any benign impact, if the first thing it does is excommunicate the sole reason for there being a 'psych-iatry' in the first place? 'Psychiatry' being derived from two Greek words – 'psyche' and 'doctor'. Again, the suspicion grows that benign impact is being nudged further down the agenda, in favour of a good solid, repeatable structure upon which all psychiatrist can agree, and through which all psychiatric patients can be thrust, like the modern equivalent of a horrendous psychiatric Procrustean Bed.

The method used by DSM-IV to dodge the issue of the mind, is straightforward old-fashioned obfuscation. Alluding to a philosophical expertise it clearly lacks, it gestures in the direction of the concept of '*mind/body dualism*'. It then correctly labels this "*a reductionistic anachronism*". If it is an anachronism, what now takes its place? The DSM-IV is content that nothing take its place. The demolition of mind is completed to its satisfaction. For cosmetic reasons it offers – "*there is much 'physical' in* 'mental' disorders." But while resolutely ignoring the latter, DSM-IV plumps heavily for the 'physical', even going so far as to state quite explicitly that the mind/body issue is resolved 100% in its favour. *"The term 'organic mental disorder' is no longer used in DSM-IV because it incorrectly implies that the other mental disorders do not have a biological basis."* ('Organic' here means based entirely on brain tissue.) Something as obviously 'non-biological' as *"death of a loved one"*, is arbitrarily and quite openly excluded. And there are still some who think that psychiatry is soundly and scientifically based, that its progress is steady and assured, in the best possible way in this best possible of all possible worlds. Perhaps second thoughts might stir.

There is a sad irony in this, since the way through to psychiatric stability is to be found in the phrase 'helping you pull yourself together'. The one component that every psychiatric patient that ever walked the planet inevitably and always has, is the desire, the intent on the part of the sufferer to stop suffering. In this, they are no different from every other individual who seeks medical help. But before rolling down the other side, there is still some mountain climbing to do, and not all of it entirely savoury at that.

Dogma 3, ignoring the software, arises inexorably from the explicit determination to concentrate on hardware, the bizarre central aim of the whole impetus of the DSM-IV. What this excludes as a matter of course, is any possible consideration of what that hardware actually does. The foregoing illustrates quite how unsuccessful it has been, indeed how unsuccessful it could always have been expected to be, and how the future looks likely to be just as bleak as the present.

As far as software is concerned, we need to consider again to the sage Dr Samuel Johnson, who as already quoted in *Emotional Health,* in 1792 averred : *"All theory is against the freedom of the will; all experience is for it."* It is not hard to see that DSM-IV has not the least difficulty in opting for 'theory', thereby letting any notion of choice, intent or free-will go hang. And yet, of course, as the above paragraph implies, this is the only available resolution of psychiatric problems – engage the patient's wish, intent and choice to sort through their tangled emotions and embark on resolving life's difficulties as fully mature, stable adults. Not only is this option available, and raring to go – but it is the one constant feature in every psychiatric patient that ever felt emotional distress. Moreover, it works, as later chapters happily indicate.

For completeness sake, I should add that the concept of Post Traumatic Stress Disorder (PTSD) is the only condition in this unsagacious volume which by definition arises as a 'reaction' to environmental events. Accordingly, it breaks ranks with the rules so carefully laid down in the introduction. PTSD was, so the story goes, compelled onto the DSM committee by a large delegation of veterans in the USA, who command considerable political influence. PTSD after all is the familiar condition known as Shell Shock in earlier wars. It provides medical evidence of quite how toxic trauma can be on the human mind. PTSD therefore represents the only element of reality that has somehow been coerced into this otherwise utterly artificial edifice. This diagnosis can have some merit – though as usual, the trauma described is invariably 'referred' from elsewhere – a point expanded later.

It just remains to complete the leg pain analogy with respect to the classification of mental health problems along the lines espoused by DSM-psychiatrists. It's as if the latter had scrupulously avoided all experience of real psychiatry, in the real world. We have already had evidence of that with respect to schizophrenia with which this chapter opened, but also in a more general medical setting with the story about osteo-arthritis of the knee.

If you were trained as I was, that arthritis occurred in the hip, but never in the knee, then it might make some sense to divide patients with painful leg joints into two entirely separate categories – those with hip pain, and those with knee pain. But even minimal exposure to the real world, and to real pathologies quickly rectifies this original misperception. Not so, sadly, with DSM-psychiatrists, who vigorously insist on housing their patients either in 'Mental Illness' or in 'Personality Disorder' wards on the basis that they represent entirely different diseases, totally other pathologies – which demonstrates an inglorious triumph of presumption over acumen. The fact that the same patient can waltz through the whole gamut of psychiatric diseases, from psychosis to neurosis, from Personality Disorder to Mental Illness, from Bipolar to anxiety disorder – all in the same afternoon – this fact plays havoc with all who insist on pigeon-holing the splendid human mind, even in its distress. Such facts, however, will never see the light of day while the DSM-IV retains its quasi-biblical authority, its power of promotion or demotion, its poisonous hold on what should be the Queen of Medical Specialties – my first medical love – psychiatry.

All this discussion of an abstruse academic tome, the DSM-IV, might seem far removed from general social concerns. To bring it closer to home, try the phrase 'mindless unfeeling robot'. If you ever get the impression that the psychiatrist of your choice is regarding you as one of these – then you need look no further to find where it came from – it comes directly from the infernal, the unreconstructed Diagnostic and Statistical Manual of Mental Disorders 4th Edition, 1994 (the DSM–IV) and its ilk.

3) THE DAMAGE IN DETAIL

a personal story

The following story leaps off the page – I received this in my email not long after starting this book. This is the real world, where real people suffer from the prejudices, blindness and the 'denials' of professional men and women. Brace yourself, it does not make easy reading.

Dear Friends,

It is with a heavy heart that I pass this sad news along to you. Only a few days ago I wrote, encouraging you to remember those who are locked away, removed from us - as if they didn't exist. It is too late to write to Chris. Please do write to his grieving mother...

God be with us, Cassie

Dear Cassie,

My sweet, precious son, Christopher Anson Brockman, passed away last night. He had been so depressed and off of his omega-3-fatty-acid found in fish oil for a few months.... I saw him last Sunday and he was not himself. He hung himself last night at 6:52 pm....

Thank you for your prayers.

Love, Cynthia---

I want you to know a bit more about Chris. I initially met his mother, when she sent a message to my address that was circulating with the anti-drug petitions we were circulating, and found our SSRI-Crusaders group. See:

http://www.petitiononline.com/lilpro
http://www.petitiononline.com/effexor
http://www.petitiononline.com/oky71

Here is the first message I received from her:

From: "Cynthia Brockman" Subject: [SSRI-Crusaders] THANKS FOR THE PETITION Date: Thu, 14 Feb 2002 19:59:57 -0600

THANKS FOR THE PETITION.

What other grass roots campaign activities are being taken and what media attention has been generated for the petition and other activities? What is the physical mailing address to which to send a contribution?

My 18 year old son is serving a life sentence for murder that he committed while on Zoloft and Adderall and Risperdal. We grieve not only the tragic loss of life, but also his life sentence for the involuntary intoxication and akathisia adverse effects resulting from iatrogenic phenomenon that caused him to be temporarily insane when he committed his offense. We are on our second appeal request for a new trial. We have post conviction new evidence that after having been discontinued from the akathisia inducing Rx, akathisia symptoms disappeared for almost a year only to reappear when Zoloft was later readministered. We have no doubt that it was the doctor prescribed medication caused the type of brain damage that destroyed his cognitive and behavioral normal functioning.

We have and are continuing to suffer beyond description from the medical malpractice and negligent prescription of SSRI's and other medications at the hands not only of the free world doctor that initially poisoned my son, but also at the hands of incompetent and negligent doctors in the penal institutions.

When will the pharmaceutical killing fields be stopped? How many more have to die as a result of these defective prescription drug products?

I am a religious volunteer who counsels inmates and am shocked at the number of prisoners who have had catastrophic adverse and toxic reactions to their medication which caused them to commit crimes. They are experiencing some of the same Rx reactions while still on some of the same doctor prescribed drugs that sent them to prison.

I will write again.

God Bless You, Cynthia Brockman

"Judgment is without mercy for those who have shown no mercy. Mercy overcomes (triumphs over) judgment." James 2:13

"Those who are planted in the house of the Lord shall flourish in the courts of God." Psalm 92:13

If this were an isolated example, if there were no other evidence to sustain what is in effect a dire indictment of the psychiatric profession, then perhaps we could pass on, and say – some must suffer so that others can flourish. But as will be obvious, the evidence is vast, cumulative and shows no sign of diminishing. Worse, as earlier chapters have shown, and this chapter further confirms– the error, the prejudice is not a flash in the pan. The whole basis of the medical profession's approach to troubled minds is fundamentally flawed – it no longer makes sense, it cannot possibly help, and it holds within its very basis, these disasters. You cannot insist the world is as you would prefer it to be, and not then suffer the consequences of being out-of-touch.

The phrase 'mindless unfeeling robot' was just mentioned – it is described first in my earlier book, *Emotional Health*. The time has come for the general population, which includes yourself gentle reader, to elect either to continue to accept the status quo in psychiatry which ultimately propagates poisonous disasters like the above, or to communicate your wish that psychiatric affairs henceforth, be conducted differently.

I should add too that the 'fish oils' mentioned could well have an ameliorating effect, counteracting the disturbance to the brain enzymes that these drugs implement, and are, perversely, designed to implement. Instances of patients insisting on smoking have been recorded, where the nicotine helps build up those enzymes psychiatric drugs have deliberately whittled down – a sort of self-medication for doctor induced disease. What a savage commentary on a profession with a closed mind.

It is not difficult to foresee the standard DSM-psychiatrist's response to this evocative story. In the first place, as mentioned, those associated with the insane are not accorded the respect they are entitled to – so it becomes easier to crush the messenger so as to be able to disregard the message. Secondly, there is currently a curt medical escape-all which my own work has repeatedly attracted. The evidence, such as the above, is merely 'anecdotal'. This label means, in essence, that since it does not appear in the 'literature' and certainly not in the psychiatric bible the DSM-IV, then professional psychiatrists can ignore it with a clear professional conscience. Ouch.

Robert Whitaker's preface

It comes as something of a relief to turn from this picture of grief and misadventure to the sober prose of Robert Whitaker, author of *Mad in America*. In my review for the New Scientist, I judged this to be *"such an important book that every psychiatrist should be compelled to read at least the preface, every year. And everyone else should then insist on them describing in writing, every year, what they're doing about it."* Having come to that conclusion then, I cannot do other now, than include that preface here, so that the reader may judge for her or himself.

MY INTEREST IN this subject, the history of medical treatments for the mad, began in a simple manner. In the summer of 1998, I stumbled onto an unusual line of psychiatric research, which I reported on for the *Boston Globe*. In order to study the "biology" of schizophrenia, American scientists were giving the mentally ill chemical agents – amphetamines, ketamine, and methylphenidate – expected to heighten their psychosis. That seemed an unusual thing to do, particularly since some of the people recruited into the experiments had come stumbling into emergency rooms seeking help. Equally striking was the response of "ex-patients" to the experiments.

They were outraged, but not particularly *surprised.*

That seemed more than a little curious – why would they not be surprised? – and then I bumped into several studies in the medical literature that really struck me as odd. Over the past twenty-five years, outcomes for people in the United States with schizophrenia have *worsened.* They are now no better than they were in the first decades of the twentieth century, when the therapy of the day was to wrap the insane in wet sheets. Even more perplexing, schizophrenia outcomes in the United States and other developed countries today are much worse than in the poor countries of the world. The World Health Organization has looked at this question repeatedly – initially, nobody could believe this disparity in outcomes – and each time it has come back with the same result. Suffer a psychotic break in a poor country like India or Nigeria, and chances are that in a couple of years you will be doing fairly well. But suffer a similar break in the United States or other developed countries, and it is likely that you will become chronically ill. Why should that be so? Why should living in a country with rich resources, and with advanced medical treatments for disorders of every kind, be so toxic to those who are severely mentally ill? Or to put it another way, why should living in countries where the poor struggle every day to find enough to eat and treatment for a mental disorder is likely to be provided by a shaman, whose armamentarium may consist of witch-doctor potions, be so helpful to recovery?

This medical failure is a profound one. More than 2 million Americans suffer from schizophrenia, and their difficult lives bring unimaginable heartache to their families, and to others who love them. Too many of the people so diagnosed end up in prison, homeless, or shuttling in and out of psychiatric hospitals. Our society

Robert Whitaker's preface

as a whole is affected by this failure as well, and in a way that we don't normally appreciate. We usually think of the financial burden: Schizophrenia, it is said, is a "disease" that costs the United States more than $45 billion annually. But there is a much deeper cost. We, as a society, are estranged from the "mad" in our midst. We fear them and their illness. We read of occasional acts of violence committed by those said to be schizophrenic, and we respond by setting up programs that focus on keeping them medicated. But is that the best response? If the medications work so well, then why do "schizophrenics" fare so poorly in the United States?

The search to understand this therapeutic failure necessarily takes one deep into history. The past becomes a foil for understanding the present. It is a journey that begins with the founding of the first hospital in the colonies by Pennsylvania Quakers in 1751, and from there one can trace a path, however winding and twisted, to the poor outcomes of today. It is also a history that contains one surprise after another. For instance, we think of the 1800s as a time when the insane were routinely chained up and neglected, and yet, in the early nineteenth century; there arose a form of humanitarian care that has never been equaled since. Go forward one hundred years, however, and the path detours into one of the darkest chapters in America's history, one that, I believe, we have never dared to fully explore. Yet it is in that dark chapter that one finds the seeds for today's failure.

What one also quickly discovers is that a history of mad medicine reveals very little about what it is like to be "crazy" or "insane," or, as we say today, "ill with schizophrenia." However, it does reveal a great deal about the society that would "cure" these patients. Medical treatments for the severely mentally ill inevitably reflect the societal and philosophical values of the day. What is the nature of man? What does it mean to be human? Where is the line between "normals" and the "mad" to be drawn? What rights do the "mentally ill" have over their own minds? The medical treatments a society employs all arise from its answers to those questions. As such, mad medicine does provide a prism through which to view a society, and that is why the poor outcomes for those diagnosed with schizophrenia raise questions, I would think, for all of us.

Robert Whitaker's preface

Robert Whitaker

Reading that book then, led to my inviting Robert himself to address the annual conference of the James Nayler Foundation, our small mental health charity, which he graciously did in 2005. This re-awakened my interest in the damage done by drugs, which led in no small measure to the writing of the present book. *Mad In America* itself is calmly written as one would expect from a professional journalist – and it should have had a profound impact on psychiatric practice in its own right. Sadly it has not. Robert tells me he expected that by highlighting the scientific literature which testifies to today's psychiatric malpractice, then the profession itself would take up the challenge, and change its ways for the better. Regrettably this has not happened.

Such professional obduracy would seem to require rather more than just objective scientific evidence to melt it – whence a book entitled *Unsafe At Any Dose* which tries to take the same endeavour a stage further. As will be clear from earlier chapters, it seeks to describe some of the factors behind this bizarre psychiatric anomaly. To this end it needs to enlist non-psychiatric help to defeat the psychiatric dogmas already identified, with the aim of deflecting the present psychiatric juggernaut onto safer lines.

There is so much written evidence detailing the damaging impact of psychiatric drugs that I do not attempt to begin even a modest survey here. Typing 'psychiatric drug damage' into Google brings 1,500,000 responses – the evidence is there a couple of clicks away, but persuading the psychiatric profession to digest it, is proving more difficult.   And this is why it becomes crucial to raise general public awareness so we can achieve a safer psychiatry. Only positive public action stands between us and the continuing damage inflicted by both psychiatric drugs and psychiatric dogma – I can see no other realistic end in sight.

My medical friend from the last chapter remarked the other day, as we sat down to our meal, that it was always a challenge reading a book which set out from a framework with which you did not agree. However, *Mad In America* which I had recently lent him was one of those *"very few books which change your view of the world."* If only the main body of psychiatrists would do and see the same.

Professor Ebmeier's presumption

When I first started this book a little over a fortnight ago, I never dreamt I would be handed on a plate enough written evidence to sink DSM-psychiatry from within. But there is it, as large as life, in the prestigious medical journal The Lancet, no less. I downloaded this from the Lancet website [thelancet.com]

The Lancet 2006; 367:153-167

DOI:10.1016/S0140-6736(06)67964-6

Recent developments and current controversies in depression

Klaus P Ebmeier email address (a) Corresponding Author Information, Claire Donaghey (a) and J Douglas Steele (b)

Summary

In this review of the last 5 years' developments in research into depression we focus on recent advances and current controversies. We cover epidemiology and basic science as well as the treatment of depression in adults in all its forms. Depression in childhood and adolescence, as well as in old age has been covered in recent Seminars in The Lancet. Depression in adulthood remains a very common and under-treated condition, resulting in a high degree of disability. Increasingly detailed knowledge about impairment of information processing in depression is being supplemented by quantitative studies of the brain processes underlying these impairments. Most patients improve with present treatments. The mechanisms of action of antidepressants are not fully understood; the hypothesis that reversing hippocampal cell loss in depression may be their active principle is a fascinating new development. Moral panic about the claim that antidepressant serotonin reuptake inhibitors cause patients to commit suicide and become addicted to their medication may have disconcerted the public and members of the medical profession. We will try to describe the considerable effort that has gone into collecting evidence to enlighten this debate.

Affiliations

(a) Division of Psychiatry, University of Edinburgh, Kennedy Tower, Morningside Park, Edinburgh, UK
(b) Department of Mental Health, University of Aberdeen, Block A, Royal Cornhill Hospital, Aberdeen, UK

Corresponding Author Information Correspondence to: Prof Klaus P Ebmeier, Division of Psychiatry, University of Edinburgh, Kennedy Tower, Morningside Park, Edinburgh, EH10 5HF, UK

As you would expect from the opening chapter of this book, the three dogmas are here faithfully subscribed to, else this team's work would never have graced the pages of so prestigious a journal. Thus emotions are described as pertaining to a *"vague notion of mood and emotion"* from which the authors are only too happy to have *'evolved'* themselves away. The 'explanation' they favour, namely *"reversing hippocampal cell loss"* is even vaguer than the emotions they dread, but this consideration does not enter into their comprehension. Perhaps it should.

Emotions are certainly mentioned, how could they not be, since patients will insist on believing that emotions play a crucial role in their mental illhealth. Fear however, and its pathological equivalent of terror decidedly are not – how could they be when the authors are primarily concerned with brain tissue, not with the most emotive and meaningful product that is mediated through that brain tissue. Why does it count for so little that in every severely depressed person I have ever treated, fear recurs in droves.

Dogma 2 is also endorsed – the word 'mind' is conscientiously excluded, as per the best standards of DSM-IV. It simply does not occur. In a seminar on psychiatry, there is not the least need felt to mention the one organ it should be concerned with above all others, especially outranking the brain. There is no need to raise the issue that the optimum gateway to the mind is by talking to it – the question does not arise, since 'mind' doesn't either. True to DSM-psychiatry form, there is a list of 'criteria for depression'. I have to say that these strike me as being entirely artificial, bearing as much practical relevance to assisting patients as a set of rubber spanners.

The fact is there is no such disease as 'depression'. It's a bit like saying "You're suffering from what we doctors call 'pain disease' ." It's laughable, or would be, were the consequences less dire. What we have here, as throughout the DSM-IV, is a list of doctor inspired symptoms, only in this case the label given to the disease itself, is also a symptom.

The whole purpose of the medical profession is to diagnose. The word comes from 'dia' – through, and 'gnose' – to know about. That is to say a diagnosis should give you something to 'know about' the disease. It is closely linked to aetiology or causative factors. Every person in the whole world solves all the medical problems that they 'know about' from their own experience. It's only when they don't know, that they seek external medical help. They come to the doctor looking for better knowledge of what ails them. To come to a DSM-psychiatrist and be told they are 'depressed' helps not a jot – what they are looking for is the 'why?', where does it come from?, what can they do about it? All they will get from a DSM-psychiatrist, such as Prof Ebmeier, is mystification. The verbal stew becomes a riot, labels are prescribed like confetti – and the whole sinks into the despair noted in chapter one.

To concretise the symptom of depression into a disease in its own right could only possibly be justified, if the doctors doing so could thereby ensure its eradication. They cannot. Indeed they have departed the ordinary clinical scene to such an extent that they no longer talk medical sense, let alone human sense. Take the last sentence in this paper before the section headed, loosely, *"treatment"*. Here it is clearly stated that *"progress"* has been made by moving away from *"understanding mood and emotion"'* which makes human sense, to *"a fuller understanding of the real obstacles that depressed patients struggle against."* The latter are the *"localised anatomical structures and neuronal symptoms."* These "anatomical structures" relate to the hippocampal cell loss mentioned in the summary above. Here you have ignoring the mind, in full flood – the brain is elevated above all else.

Now I have an opinion, to which I am entitled – Prof Ebmeier and his ilk, hold opinions to which they are equally entitled. But when these opinions differ, as they do here, that difference should be clearly stated, so that you the customer, can sensibly choose. On the one hand I would recommend talk therapy, with an emphasis on explaining how denial works, and how it operates in your particular case – in Robert Whitaker's phrase, the 'Healing Hand of Kindness'. On the other, you can have your mental distress discussed in terms of your cingulate gyrus, or your hippocampal cells. You can be made to feel welcomed, to feel at home – or you can ask to see the scans that demonstrate the brain tissue lesions which Prof Ebmeier and his colleagues assert is your real problem. Prof Ebmeier abominates the "vague notions of mood and emotion" which I, as a talk therapist, celebrate. The choice is between these two. The choice is there, it is stark, and it's up to you, since as a result of the factors already discussed, the profession itself, including the editor of The Lancet have already made clear which they prefer.

It would be unwise to think that 'science' will make this choice for you. The medical model pursued by DSM-psychiatrists readily catches the ear of medical editors, as the full 10 pages in the Lancet testifies. Though repeatedly asserting that they value scientific evidence – Robert Whitaker's endeavours show that their understanding of that evidence, when it impacts their cherished dogmas, is kept carefully circumscribed.

What is going on here is a contest for the soul of psychiatry. Do you favour the 'Healing Hand of Kindness' or do you prefer the concretisms of DSM-psychiatrists? The choice is there for you to make. But in the present circumstances, it is not sufficient for you only to choose – I'm sorry to have to tell you, you also have to act. Professor Ebmeier and his colleagues command the heights of current psychiatry. He and his ilk dominate the scene and ensure their view is heard, while simultaneously ensuring that more humane views are not.

Look closely at the summary cited above, and this more sinister aspect emerges. Professor Ebmeier declares –

"Moral panic about the claim that antidepressant serotonin reuptake inhibitors cause patients to commit suicide and become addicted to their medication may have disconcerted the public and members of the medical profession. We will try to describe the considerable effort that has gone into collecting evidence to enlighten this debate."

One wonders what professor Ebmeier and his ilk would make of the views expressed by Cynthia above, who states that she is "a religious volunteer who counsels inmates and am shocked at the number of prisoners who have had catastrophic adverse and toxic reactions to their medication which caused them to commit crimes. They are experiencing some of the same Rx reactions while still on some of the same doctor prescribed drugs that sent them to prison."

There is almost a palpable rejection of raw clinical evidence which gainsays the DSM-psychiatrist's hard won 'stability'. If the evidence is there, and the profession keeps finding excuses to prevent such evidence from having its proper impact – who is left who will ensure that it does so?

Again, were I a professor of philosophy I would wonder at the use of the word *'moral'* in this context. I would worry too that the views of the people who actually consume these products, and who are clearly noted to have become 'disconcerted', are firmly put in their place. This place is not at the centre of affairs – where the patient sits, or certainly should sit in every other

Professor Ebmeier's presumption

medical context anywhere else in the world. No, here the professor and his team describe *"the considerable effort that has gone into collecting evidence to enlighten this debate"*. As I read this, "enlighten" here means to relieve any panic, moral or otherwise. The evidence collected in this seminar I have now read through very carefully – and I have to conclude that there is absolutely nothing to reassure me, or others as above who have suffered from the toxic effects of these drugs. The evidence, though wished for in this summary, is simply absent from the text.

What is there, is a blithe endorsement of Electro Convulsive Treatment (ECT) – something which again, has accumulated more evidence of damage than you could imagine. But as is the common pattern now in today's DSM-psychiatry, this evidence is no longer to the fore, and indeed is finessed away with a smoothness that almost amounts to a skill. Denial clearly takes many different and highly imaginative forms.

shocking electrical 'treatment'

Professor David Healy of Bangor University has written widely on depression. He is a well established expert in this field, and he had no difficulty at all in persuading the judge that my protestations against Electro Convulsive Treatment (ECT) were decidedly passé. He assured the court that since Dr Johnson's day, 'we' now knew a great deal more about depression. He mocked my more humanitarian stance, by indicating that I had clearly got stuck in the 1980s, or before. The judge, as judges will, elected for the status quo – he concluded that the damage suffered by my client, which was dramatic, had not been caused by negligence of the Health Authority under whose auspices the ECT had been administered.

I wrestled and struggled on the court room stand – I regret I did not have the incisive legal skills that my friend Dr Peter Breggin could have brought to bear so effectively – if I had, perhaps the outcome might have been different. Though again, given the intransigence of the current English medico-legal system, perhaps not.

The case in question involved a woman who had been a taxi driver for over 20 years – which meant she had not the least difficulty in handling traffic, coinage and locations without which driving a taxi is impossible. She had a number of domestic problems, and during one of these she ended up in hospital. While there, she was given a course of 6 ECTs. While driving back, after the 3rd or 4th, she developed a ferocious headache, stopped at a traffic light, and suddenly did not know where she was, or how to get where she was going.

It appears that I was the only consultant psychiatrist in the UK at that time, who would stand up against this barbaric treatment – 'brain damage as miracle therapy' as Robert Whitaker would have put it. So, sadly, when Professor Healy demolished my medical standing, and paved the way for the defeat of my client's claim for compensation, or at least for recognition, he also halted the legal process for correcting this appalling mediaeval method of 'treating' people who are suffering. It is now no longer possible to challenge ECT in English courts, legal aid no longer supports doing so, and the many sufferers being necessarily unemployable – cannot afford to run the cases themselves.

I have now prepared reports on a dozen or so cases where the damage caused by ECT is staggering. These vary from a young engineer no longer being able to tell the time, to an intelligent woman no longer able to learn new card games – "Don't look at the card that's dropped on the floor," said her partner. "Don't worry," says she, "I'll have forgotten it as soon as I've picked it up". A table summing these is available on our website www.TruthTrustConsent.com, at the end of an 'informed consent form' which I drew up for ECT.

My taxi driver not only lost the ability to determine where she was, or where she was going – she could no longer count. When I videoed an interview with her later, hoping to persuade a television company to show her plight, I pulled out a handful of change from my pocket and asked her to count it. She got it wrong. From being an outgoing person 'the life and soul of the party', she is now a virtual recluse, unemployable and alone.

As I examined more and more cases of post-ECT damage, it became clear that the ECT was destroying small pockets of the brain, and thereby dissecting out which bits did what. There are, from my clear observations, parts of the brain concerned with calculations, others with telling the time, yet others with the detail of social interactions. The problem is, there is no way of knowing where these small, and vital pockets are – the application of electric current to brain tissue is entirely at random. The damage it does is also quite impossible to predict.

There is a tight medical argument concerning the nature of epilepsy, which is what ECT inflicts in the healthy brain. The key diagnostic feature of epilepsy is amnesia – when a person came to me as a general practitioner and said they had 'fainted', what I needed to ascertain immediately was – what did they immediately remember? If they wobbled over, and could remember falling, and then remember coming round, the chance of there being the sinister disease of epilepsy was reduced to insignificance. However, if they could not remember quite what they were doing immediately before, nor fully recall precisely what happened for half an hour or so afterwards – then my medical duty was clear – full investigations for epilepsy were imperative.

Thus epilepsy entails amnesia, disturbance of memory. Ergo, ECT does the same. Doctors blithely assure patients that this amnesia is short lived, but that's because they have decided not to review the longer term evidence. Another instance of 'quick-fix psychiatry'. It is now clear to me that ECT 'works', when it does, by ensuring that the person receiving it 'forgets' what caused their depression, indeed what they feared. Again there are safer more reliable ways of easing fears than bombarding brain tissue with random shafts of damaging electric shocks.

My excursion into the medico-legal implications of ECT taught me several unpleasant truths. For one thing, I found precisely the same ability to finesse adverse scientific evidence there as elsewhere. And for another, it became clear that since the law prefers precedent and the status quo, it failed to offer a sensible avenue by which to achieve psychiatric reform. As regards the first, I was shaken by Professor Healy's ability to gloss over the damage ECT does – I had thought he would have been better prepared to inform the wider public, including the law, of its inherently damaging nature. Sadly he was not. The other medical authority who also astonished me was Professor Hugh Freeman, erstwhile editor of the British Journal of Psychiatry.

In a report to a prominent QC who was conducting the defence of a different case at another Health Authority, Professor Freeman states categorically – *"there is no evidence from animal experiments that ECT . . . . causes neuropathological changes"*. This is breath taking. So many animal studies were conducted during the 1950s and 60s, and the results were so conclusive, that it was thought that further such experiments could no longer be justified on ethical grounds – enough data had already been gathered to prove the matter beyond doubt. Brain damage is inherent in any toxic agent that penetrates the several layers of the skull, and manages to impact on the cerebral tissue below. Micro-haemorrhages are commonplace, long term scarring inevitable. The brain does not like to be traumatised, the body goes to considerable lengths to protect it – when these protections are breached, damage is inevitable.

In my comments on Professor Freeman's report, I suggested that his ignorance of this abundant contrary evidence demonstrated with staggering clarity "the fixity of the orthodox psychiatric position, which entails steadfastly minimising medical and animal evidence of gross harm." My comments carried little legal weight – established professors prefer the status quo, since it was through that route that they gained their ascendancy. Mavericks who proffer change, can easily be disposed of. The phrase I found myself using is – having climbed to the top of the tree, they don't want to be told it's the wrong tree. My 'telling' has gone as far as I can take it – others must now pick up the baton, for there to be any chance of rescuing whole generations of emotional sufferers.

anorexia from the inside

Next follows another personal story – this time with a happier outcome. This is Kate, whose poems appear at the end of *Emotional Health*. The consultant in charge of her at the hospital was said to be a world expert in anorexia. He had heard of my work, and advised the family that it would be dangerous to refer Kate to me. In the event, as you may read, the outcome was rather more favourable. Here then is an example of what happens if you do use talk as a means of communicating with the human mind. This is the description Kate gave when I asked her recently to describe what happened and what it was like from the inside. When time and resources permit, I hope to compile a training video demonstrating how this came about, so that others can benefit from it. With intelligent, fast thinking people, it is essential to maintain a strong bond of trust before you begin. Here is Kate's story.

After a holiday in Crete, where I had already started experimenting with under-eating, I remember distinctly the summer barbecue at a neighbour's had me in fits of tears about my weight; this was the day I decided to starve my body into submission.

I was the oldest child, very academic, and came into puberty at ten or eleven. Being the sort of child who liked to please her parents, I was terrified my body wasn't something I could readily control, and that womanhood brought the anxieties and depressions that I saw my mother struggling with. Through the last year of primary and the first year of secondary school I was tormented by close friends about being more 'grown up' than them and had the feeling of being sorely conspicuous amongst my peer group; I guess that the consistent build up of negative reactions to my maturing body triggered the drastic measures I took to remain in a child's guise.

Even when I had lost a considerable amount of weight, and my parents especially were commenting on how thin I looked, the drive to lose more didn't subside. In all ways I had retreated into myself, become completely closed off socially and emotionally, and intensely obsessed with what was measurable in my life: calories and kilos lost. I lived in a sort of coma, full of white noise, without feeling anything but fear. I was so afraid to stop or be stopped because I believed there was nothing outside of my bubble; bursting my impenetrable pupa would kill me - thrust out in a world where time would undo me. I could see the pain of others around me (my brothers too waiting in dread of what I might do next) but felt there was nothing I could do to relieve them of their guilt and worry and panic; I thought that the root of it all was outside of me, was something out of my control. Getting me out of my 'vacuum' and into a hospital was a lot of trouble for my parents, who pleaded for advice from various health professionals for many weeks before I was finally assessed by one of my mum's colleagues. I was admitted the same day, needless to say, because I was in such a bad state physically. Much of the initial information gathered about my condition at the time has been relayed to me; I was only really aware of feeling relieved at not having to think about my schoolwork, and the rows at home, which had been increasing as my weight fell.

I was glad too for my parents, who now wouldn't have to worry that their fourteen year old was starving, but instead being fed and monitored and counselled, as you would expect any child with a life-threatening disorder to be treated. Alas, it was a different story in reality! I was weighed every few days, but in between it was entirely up to me whether to eat, or exercise, or cheat my weight, or cut myself - the 'care' I received from that first hospital could be packaged and wrapped up in a box labelled 'Minimal intervention - miscellaneous condition - do not treat because we don't know how'! One day I would be hooked up to a monitor telling them my heart rate was worryingly low, and that actually I might slip into a coma tonight, and the next without any further tests I could be doing a bit of frantic pacing after no breakfast or lunch, and chatting to the nurses about not really 'fancying' dinner without raising any real concern. I was once seen by the local child psychiatrist with my parents present, was thoroughly humiliated by his demeaning and inappropriate questions, burst into tears through the part when he insisted that a Section was my parents' best option, and can't really remember anything else he said - he treated me like I was possessed, and wouldn't it be nicer for everyone if I was contained in a proper little unit where they would know how to 'deal' with me. It was clear that the hospital was not equipped for helping patients with psychiatric conditions, but once they had admitted me, their medical intervention was elementary.

Luckily my mum is a paediatric nurse, had some connections at a different hospital, and we escaped with my things, pretending to go to the hospital shop, whilst my dad distracted the nurses. This was about the time I realised the incompetence of the professionals around me and the journey through various other hospitals and specialist units became a game, trying to convince them I was well and gaining weight - that they should let me go - and this was not uncommon, for the girls to pull the wool over the nurses' eyes in a collective effort to outwit the system. I became a very good anorexic during my inpatient treatment. I had no intention of putting on any significant amount of weight and in fact had quite a good time devising ways to hide food, putting things in my socks to cheat at weigh-in, exercising vigorously between 'checks' and banging a drum in therapy sessions to relieve the abstract anger they were at pains to point out. No one addressed the disorder with any passion or hope for recovery - a senior nurse snidely remarked that she'd see me again in a few months time, after I'd relapsed - and the general consensus was that to get any sense out of an anorexic you'd have to wait until you'd fed her back to a normal weight. Force feeding via a naso-gastric tube was often used, bulimic patients had access to their private toilets too soon after meals, many nurses were untrained in eating disorders and let it go by them when we hid food, poured drinks away and kept glass bottles for self-harm. I'm sure that most of them thought we should 'just eat'. I was amused by the therapy offered me, with its talk of 'managing' the disorder - I wanted to live as an anorexic or get out completely.

My day-patient care after leaving the specialist unit was dire. I was alone when eating, and my therapy sessions were ways of passing time until I left in the evening. I really didn't have much trust in improving my situation in the long term, after transferring to outpatient care at a different hospital, because my consultant treated anorexia as a biological demon that couldn't be exorcised. My weight dropped and my confusion rose - three months after leaving a five month inpatient treatment I was at a lower weight than when I had been admitted. I think a lot of people were ready to put me back into hospital and I have to say that their resignation to my illness did not instil a belief that I could escape it. But even as I sat in a room with my mother and my consultant, talking into his Dictaphone about my deterioration like I was just a naughty little girl, I felt I knew from my session with Bob (whom I had seen once before I went into that first hospital) that anorexia didn't have to be chronic.

I had been tricking them all for a chance to get out of hospital and try and see Dr. Bob on a regular basis - I started doing this I think the winter after I turned fifteen, with great success and a sense of independence, travelling between London and York on my own, proving the sceptical consultant wrong. I began to see that I wasn't a stupid and insolent child with an incurable disease but an adult with a fear of surviving without her parents.

Scott Maloney

"Wait," cried Dame Fiona Caldicott, then President of the Royal College of Psychiatrists, as she bounced down the aisle. "Wait. We have political power. We can prevent the closing of your Special Unit, in Parkhurst Prison. Just write to us." The time – 1995. The place – Torquay. The occasion – the Royal College of Psychiatrists' Annual Conference. I had just finished describing how Emotion Support worked for violent prisoners in Parkhurst Prison, and had shown the full 16 minutes of Lenny's video the dialogue for which appears in chapter five.

Dame Fiona was animated. She was inspired. She had just witnessed irrefutable visual evidence of a dramatic change in the very personality of a criminal. Along with 100 or so other psychiatrists, she had been gripped by the story which had unfolded that hour – you could have heard a pin drop. Alas, it was not to be. Of course I wrote – I wrote to half a dozen eminent authorities in that organisation, and received not a single reply. The office staff thought I was 'in', so encouraged me to organise the 'Family' section of the next Annual Conference, and told me who to write to, to confirm that. No joy. I was being treated to the rather English way of leaving unwanted projects to wither on the vine – say nothing, and hope it goes away. Most discourteous.

The C-Wing Special Unit at Parkhurst Prison was a remarkable exception to the invariably counter-productive way British prisons are currently run. An account of the results obtained there is included in the Appendix.

The Special Unit was closed anyway – yet another casualty of the sub-feudal nature of British government. A BBC Panorama programme of my work there was shown, on 3 March 1997, having run the gauntlet of the Home Secretary ringing the BBC Director General telling him to stop transmission, and when that failed, of seeking a High Court injunction against it. A somewhat battered programme was finally transmitted, being seen by 3□ million people, yet its impact on British penal policy was nil. (Dame Fiona crossed my path again during my eviction from Ashworth – an abbreviated reference to which is included in my letter to The Lancet that was published, and is also included in the Appendix.)

If I can once command a public spotlight, I will shine it on the disgraceful state of affairs which our moribund psychiatry engenders in our so-called Maximum Security Hospitals. An unhappy miscegenation between political expedience, populism and venal psychiatry leads to a situation there which mimics Soviet psychiatry more closely than any civilised society should tolerate. Do not judge your county by how it behaves in sunny weather – check out the unprivileged, the prisons, and especially those prisons which masquerade as hospitals. Scott is a kind of litmus paper for this desperate state of affairs – a living proof of inhumanity as practised by an ossified psychiatry, implementing abysmal government policies, without demur.

I first met Scott in 2000. He was involved in a gruelling family court case, some of whose details are included in *Emotional Health* – a book written in that year, which could therefore take no account of the depths to which the matter subsequently sank. The judge in that case managed to alienate the entire nascent family, leading to an outburst of violent rage and assault by Scott when drunk. For this crime, he was sentenced to 6 years, of which he was due to serve 4. On August 1st 2004, he expected to be released. In June of that year he found himself in Rampton Maximum Security Hospital. He asked his solicitor how long he was going to be there – "how long is a piece of string", replied his solicitor, unhelpfully.

Scott's problems had begun when, aged 5, his father had deserted the family. There was buried rage, and indeed fear associated with this, together with a desperate need to keep families together. Against this background, the interventions by Social Services and by the Family Court were unduly punitive. Nevertheless Scott attended my then clinic in York, and was making sterling progress. He latched onto my way of looking at things, and continued to keep regularly in contact with me, up to the present day.

I was next asked to see him in March 2004, and argued as strongly as I could against him being transferred to Rampton which was then on the cards. There were, I stated, "*clear medical indications for NOT transferring him to maximum security conditions at this time. I do not believe that he fulfils the criteria set out in the Mental Health Acts, either with regard to his having a mental disorder within the meaning of the Act, or of displaying, or risking displaying abnormally aggressive and seriously irresponsible behaviour. Nor does he fulfil the treatability clause, since he has consistently declared his refusal to cooperate with any treatment that might be offered him under maximum security conditions, a refusal which receives my vigorous medical support.*"

Needless to say, Scott now languishes in Rampton. Asked when he can expect to return to the community, he is told he must undergo some eight years 'treatment'. His most recent tribunal agreed with the resident Consultant that he not be released. He is currently helping to fill the new 'Dangerous Severe Personality Disorder (DSPD)' Unit there, a unit which the government prolifically funds, on the flimsiest medical grounds. Some £270,000,000 are being squandered on making bad situations gravely worse. Rational thinking is suffocated, distorted reasoning prevails – and the problems become ever deeper, ever more rancorous, and verge ever closer to the grossly uncivilised, where the wrong things seem to happen as a matter of course.

When he heard of this book, he asked me to be sure to put his point of view. Here is the letter he wrote to me:

Scott Maloney To Dr Bob Johnson 24th January 2006

This letter is From our last phone call this month Jan 06.

As you're Aware, I was knocked back on my M.H.R.T. Tribunal. There should be a copy of the tribunal's decision, enclosed For you.

Dr Bob Johnson, I will now go into some details - from when I first came onto the D.S.P.D. unit, dated from the 3rd Feb 05.

I was on Derwent, the I.C.U., intensive-care-unit, there was My Attempted escape, then I was transferred to the D.S.P.D. unit on the 3rd Feb 05. Due to my 'Risks and subversive ways (Breachers).

As soon as I arrived onto the Peaks D.S.P.D. unit, I again declared my Full-Refusal to engage with treatment and still haven't engaged. For now My full stay at Rampton altogether for 19- Months now right back from My Admission date which was 10th June-2004, basically, there was only 6 weeks left till My Prison-Release-date.

Anyway Dr Johnson, I will tell You in my own words why I won't engage in treatment.

My Reason's are....

One – when I was in the community - living a violent-free life - with Michelle My girlfriend and our Daughter Lauren, she was My Step-Daughter, but at that time Michelle was pregnant with My First baby, My daughter-Chloe.

I was interrupted by Social-services and Psychiatrists – that was when you Dr-Bob-Johnson become involved in My life.

I was Assessed by you in person, and I was Receiving treatment from your clinic in York. I did find the treatment so Much of benefit to me, but-Due to a lot of frustration and Due to the stress from the Mental Health Act authorities and Psychiatrist involved with the social-services, I could not take it anymore. I committed an offence of Section 18-wounding on a innocent Man, As he was trying to protect his neighbours plant pot.

I received 5 years and I pleaded Guilty for my offence. I have Genuine Remorse for my Actions and wrong-doings.

So my life and future went from bad to worst.

This one important thing why I do not trust the Mental Health Act workers authorities, this is why I will not engage at all, or ever with treatment whilst in Rampton D.S.P.D. unit.

I believe the only therapy I may have benefited from in the past was Dr Bob Johnson due to his Approaches that he Dr Johnson was there to help me, and support me, he was not there to make matters worst for me, he was there to help me.

I asked Staff at Rampton on the D.S.P.D. unit, where I am held at the Moment....
>If I engage in treatment, can you Guarantee Me, that I will be left alone, when I am Released From here, and not destroy My life, My Future or Family.

I got no Guarantees From Rampton Authorities, or Rampton D.S.P.D.S. Authorities.

So this is the real reason For my non-engagement.
Whilst here at Rampton D.S.P.D unit.

Due to My non-engagement whilst here at Rampton Hospital and on here the D.S.P.D unit, I have been Sexually Touched up, whilst been searched by STAFF, and they Grab My Chest Area, and Laugh and say I have a big chest, I think this is inappropriate.

I File complaints against STAFF, but My complaints are turned down, As the Managers believe their own Staff and not Me, coz I am a patient here in Rampton.

I have threats From Nursing Staff, like if I don't engage in treatment, I will be locked up For life and I will never ever be Released, even though I no longer have a prison sentence left, or any Home Office Restrictions on me.

The only person who can Release Me is My R.M.0. Doctor, but I believe he will not Release Me, coz by Me being locked up, it is in the best interest in protecting the Public From me.

I Just don't understand, What happened to the best interest of the Patient?

This System is wrong, it's degrading, and very Punitive, I feel like I'm in Prison and I'm a prisoner.

There is no difference, between here and prison.

I am convinced, I do not engage in treatment For Reasons already mentioned.

I sit in the day area on the unit, listen to music, and that's it.

I Just can't believe that who ever is paying for Me to be Just locked up here in the D.S.P.D. unit, i.e. funding Tax payers Money, they are wasting an estimate of £180.000 a year on me alone per Patients. I Ask why is this sum of Money wasted on Me, when I will never do treatment.

There are a lot of Patients who are held against their will – like Me, but other Patients engage coz they see no other way.

Yes Patients engage and are Motivated to engage in treatment, but when I Ask many patients here on the Rampton D.S.P.D. unit, their Reasons for engaging in treatment, their Answer is to get out, so the Patients do their treatment and get out – move on to R.S.U'S, then I Ask the Patients – will you Re-offend once you leave Rampton?

Scott Maloney

The Patients answer I'll do what I want, coz then I'm out of Rampton Hospital.

I would say from My own experience and From talking to a large number of patients, here held on the Rampton D.S.P.D. unit,

A lot of patients who are and will be released From here, will Re-offend, or be Recalled back to Hospital.

This system here is forced.

It Forces patients to engage in treatment – but For the wrong reasons. I believe in the long Run, the Rampton D.S.P.D. unit services will not be a success.

There already has been one Patient Released from here into a hostel, that patient Re-Offended after only 3 days out in the community, that person is now 'Locked' back up in a Young Offenders Prison.

(So Me success that person Received)

There are Many patients here who are assaulted by Staff whilst being inappropriately restrained. that I witness with my own two eyes, Staff have a good Laugh when they have got the patient into seclusion.

I see this on a Regular basis, this alone damages My health and others who witness it.

I was Recently Assaulted by Nursing staff on the 2nd January 2006, I Received bruises to my eye-face and both arms. I have had photos taken of the injuries, and gave a statement to the police. All I can hope now For is, that these nursing Staff don't Assault Me again.

I personally think the Matter won't go any Further- or that the Staff will continue to Abuse these powers, and Assault Me and others at will.

Sometimes I think of committing serious offences here on staff – Just to try and get back to prison, coz this place is sending me insane.

A lot of times I wanted to punch Staff's Faces in, but Managed to control Myself.

I have personally gone now over 5☐ years, from not committing violent Act's on any person, this is not Due to me being locked up in Prison or Hospital, it's coz of my own choice.

But I Question Myself, How Much longer do I have to do here? I feel that there will come a time for me, where the only answer for ME, is to commit offences and keep on committing offences, until these staff/Authorities throw me back in prison with some sort of prison sentence. I Just can't believe that I Might have to be Forced into a situation to Just stay locked up here forever, or to go back to prison, or try at least. I do prefer to go back to prison, As this place is not for Me.

I Feel so exhausted of trying to tell these nursing staff, that I don't want to engage in treatment – ever, but I'm not heard. So what am I left with,
! <u>You tell Me</u> !

Dr. Bob Johnson, I hope My letter can help you understand me, and My feelings.

I give you permission to use my letter, in any way you would like to.

I hope you Reply to me A.S.A.P.
Just to let Me know you got my letter.

    Thanks

Scott Maloney

P.S.   Take Care
Say hello   Dr.Bob
To Sue
  Thanks

If a patient in an 'ordinary hospital' described conditions such as these, there should surely be a public outcry. Here we have a prisoner who has completed the sentence the judge gave him, contemplating further violence in order to get away from the 'hospital' he never wished to enter in the first place. An Augean stable, not safely in some Greek myth of long ago, but in the heart of our own 'civilised' country today.

Worse, in conversation with Scott the other day, he tells me that all restrictions imposed on him and on his young family have been lifted – six years after they were imposed. Without these, he would never have given vent to the rage which lead to his index offence. Without these he could have continued to attend my then clinic in York, which he clearly enjoyed. The family judge went out of his way to be discourteous to me – is there any audit on how he judged the matter so ill? Is there any mechanism to assist him to learn his trade better, so that he protects those in real danger, and limits the damage he inflicts on those not.

Time to leave these dreadful dungeons, and the ill-advised misadventures of the law and see what could be better done, review how the human mind really functions, and what a safer psychiatry would actually look like. Safer that is, for Scott and his ilk, but, equally important, for the rest of society, including dear reader, ourselves.

4) SAFER PSYCHIATRY

a guided tour of the human mind

I cannot read your mind. No psychiatrist can, nor ever will. I can't even look into it very well. What I can do is invite you to look into it for me. And this is the key not only to a safer psychiatry, but to a saner world, and indeed to something we all crave beyond anything else – peace of mind.

These two factors need always to be born in mind – if they are minimised or overlooked, then progress in exploring the mind will be hampered or impossible. Your mind is your own, no one can read it, nor even control it very well – you are what matters when it comes to minds, in particular to your mind. That's the first thing. The second is that you can share your mental furniture, if and only if you wish, or decide to do so. The benefit of sharing your thoughts and feelings is that you have them validated. And without validation our mental stability first wobbles, then bits start to fall off, which threatens our social cohesion, thence jeopardising our very survival.

I am happy to offer a guided tour of the human mind – I have been conducting a really long expedition into mental territory most of my life, some 70 years now. But the first thing to do is to insist on the things you not bring with you. Just as when visiting the world's finest works of art, you are now likely to be frisked for possible destructive packages – so when exploring what is undoubtedly the most brilliant, delightful, fascinating entity on earth – there are one or two items which you would be better off without, and whose absence will make my task on this guided tour that much easier.

So don't bring any dogma. No, not even one small dogma sitting quietly in the corner. No dogmas allowed. It is easy to see why.

We are about to explore the most flexible, dynamic, ever changing, elastic process even known, and you want to bring in a rigid statement, a fixed text, an unshiftable inflexible belief or creed. Well of course, you are in charge of what you bring, but think first. Would you go to a fantastic concert, only to keep your ears plugged, listening to your own iPod? Would you visit a great art gallery, and keep your eyes glued to a magazine all the time? Dogma is the human attempt to fix things in an ever changing world – and sadly the first thing that's fixed or rather gummed up, is human mental creativity, which represents the only possible escape hatch.

So why should you set aside your most cherished beliefs? Well this brings in the next ingredient – trust. There is simply no way you would even consider re-arranging your mental foundation stones, if you doubted the value in doing so. I wouldn't dream of asking you to, unless I had first built up a level of trust which could support such a radical move. Now trust is a social commodity. It even has a financial value, as witness the loss of it in the currency of the Weimar republic, or in other instances of hyperinflation. But you can't buy trust – you can only earn it. It's hard to gain, and oh so easy to lose. Together with Truth and Consent, it is explored further in my earlier book *Emotional Health*.

Trust is hard enough to build up in the real world, where people can talk, touch and communicate with each other – it's even harder through the pages of a book. It is only possible if we think of this as a stylised conversation. It's a bit lopsided admittedly, but I am suggesting things, you consider them, I then suggest something else, and if you wish to continue the 'conversation' you continue to struggle to make out what I am trying to say. Ho hum, a bit of a long-winded affair, but that's all we've got at the moment, so here goes.

So if we exclude dogma, as much as we humanly can, what are we left with? Well immediately there's a void – out there things are always shifting, change is the order of the day. In terms of physics – entropy or disorganisation is always on the increase. Not however in living organisms, which for some totally unfathomable reason defy this law of nature – organisms organise, their entropy does not inexorably increase – except when they die, when it promptly does so. It's curious how dogma prevents so many 'scientists' from seeing this glorious fact, this miracle of life.

Living processes can organise themselves, heal cuts, knit leg bones – we don't need to know how, we just need to exploit this miracle to the full. Translating that into the mental sphere, we know that human beings are capable of organising – they can do things, they can bring order where there was none before, they can create patterns out of chaos. They do this, not by being inflexible or dogmatic, which is inevitably out of date before the ink is dry – no, they do this because they are flexible, creative, organisable. So when things are falling apart, when our minds are breaking down – we need somehow to plug into a reliable, trustworthy supply of mental stability, mental reliability, non-dogmatic flexible mental support.

These then are the preliminaries – omit dogma and grow trust; the one leads to the need for the other. Without trust, this 'conversation' becomes a monologue, if not mute: with it, you can begin to swallow, provided you have first approved the taste, as advised in the maxim from the opening chapter. Don't wait for 'science' or other grand theology to decide the issue for you – they are talking about something else from a different time frame, which overlaps with you and me only at the margins, if at all. Keep as open a mind as you can, gather views and contentions from as wide a field as is available to you, and make your own mind up – it's safer that way, and you will know just how much reliance to put on the final result.

So what are the features we can all agree upon, having set our dogmas aside? We've covered two already – the need for you to invite me, or anyone else to look into your mind with you, and then the indispensable supply of trust. The first we can label 'consent', the second, well, trust. Armed with these two stalwarts, we survey the scene.

The most striking feature of minds is their creativity. They can imagine a whole series of remarkable things: they can create notions, ideas, tunes, themes, motifs, even crack jokes, which simply were not there before. The philosophical tag for this, is creation *de novo*, from new. Of course they cannot do this, if the dogma of a rigid deterministic universe holds sway – but when it doesn't, they can. The only other item I need to draw your attention to, is emotion. These thoughts, schemas, mental concepts and conceits – move. Something moves them about, labels them 'good' or 'bad', giving them values as it does so – this motion we call emotion.

Now, as all best guides do, I shall leave you to marvel at the wonders listed already – they stand on their own two feet, they are remarkable enough in their own right without needing embellishment from me. Emotions however require further comment. They cannot be defined, the more you tie them down, the less meaning you are left with.

So the pragmatic thing to do is grasp the key emotion, take a firm hold of the Master Emotion – give that a good tugging, and all the others fall into place. Or rather, remove fear, which of course is allocated the number one slot, and all the happier emotions are quite capable of taking care of themselves. But beware of denial, which takes any strength it has from fear – indeed by removing the fear, the denial becomes superfluous, and the 'denyer' grows to see the same world you do; which is always a bonus all round.

Fear invariably has the same fundamental base – in whichever human mind it occurs, it is always fundamentally about the same thing. In the ultimate it asks – "Will I survive?" All the lesser fears, the anxieties, the worries, the panics, the phobias are really pale reflections of that fundamental question. And as such, they can be answered in the affirmative, given enough supply of Trust, coupled with adequate amounts of Truth, and always with sufficient Consent.

This might sound a bit like a dogma. So don't take my word for it – find out if this is true for yourself. But before you dismiss it out of hand, seek out and find someone you can trust enough to invite to look into your mind with you. It's something our current chief Emotion Support Worker works at all the time. Anyone can learn to do it. That's the beauty of it. What it needs is sufficient tact, courtesy, flexibility and diplomacy – and a conviction that adult emotions are more realistic than infantile ones, that everyone wants to become more mentally secure, more self-confident and thereby better able to support their own mental stability and contribute significantly to the stability of others. It's what human society is all about, from families to the whole human race.

For many, the world seems far too indeterminate, things fall apart, chaos constantly corrodes, nothing seems fixed or secure. Don't look for security in texts, nor in dogmas – pursue the dynamic mental stability just described, which relies on creativity, on truth, trust and consent. In other words look into other people's minds for validation, for emotional security, and thence for peace of mind.

consent/intent as housekeeper

As discussed in *Emotional Health,* it is pragmatic to regard consent and intent as first cousins. Pragmatic in the sense that if you press these two mysteries too far, all you get is deeper into the mire. Though not as deep as you sink if your dogma tells you that you have no choice, no ability to choose – that your every move, your every thought is Fully Determined by the one before, and can never vary from what has been laid down aeons ago, by the cosmic clockmaker.

In the brief guided tour just described, intent was subsumed under consent. Without your consent, any such tour is hampered or impossible. However, we humans are fundamentally sociable beings, at least that's how we're born, indeed we make our evolutionary mark by socialising rather than by living in unsplendid isolation. So there is a keen thrust towards social contacts, to making social ties and towards keeping them in good repair. This allows us to flourish as a human race, and it also turns out to be indispensable for our sanity.

Now what intent actually is, or how it really comes about, I have not the faintest idea. I know it is a function of being alive, I know it defies the entropy to which all non-living systems are prone, and I further know that no amount of delving into the inner recesses of the brain will 'prove' the matter either way. But further than that I would not wish to go. I experience the ability to choose. I do it regularly in the supermarket, the advertising industry flourishes on the basis that it can influence my intentions, and every few years or so, my government asks me to exercise a democratic choice by ballot – none of these would happen if I did not have a measure of freedom by which to choose. It is as well to recall Dr Samuel Johnson again – *"All theory is against the freedom of the will – all experience is for it"*. It rather depends where you want to live – in a theoretical world, where rules, and scientific or religious laws hold sway – or in the world you experience every waking moment.

Earlier I suggested that the function of the mind was to guide you as to what to do next. Here I would like to take the matter a step further. Existentialism is the philosophy which says we exist first, and everything else, including all our florid theories about that, comes a poor second. This philosophy has a somewhat bohemian image, prone to anarchy which is not entirely to my taste. I propose Nexistentialism to indicate that all acts must be responsible and take into account what might happen next – that is, if we wish to prolong or indeed enhance our survival. In other words, our reasoning enables us to contemplate what might happen next, and to take steps to accentuate that or avoid it, depending on what we decide, or indeed what our wider intentions are.

Now intent looks forward in this way. But it also has a vital function to perform in ensuring we keep our mental model of what's out there, up to date. In a sense, it is like a housekeeper, tidying up the bits and pieces which come into our minds, sorting through our various experiences and drawing what conclusions it can from that. Again I have no idea what it is, but a very clear idea of what happens when it isn't working very well, or it misses its mark for some other reason. For when this happens, clarity of thinking goes, life becomes unduly burdensome, and you really do begin to wonder what to do next, for the best.

The key factor which disrupts this smooth passage of thought, the velvet progression from where we are now, to where we would like to be in a little while, is the Master Emotion – fear. And from fear it is a small step to nailing down the source of all dogma, each and every dogma that ever came into anybody's mind.

Fear not only obliterates further thought – this is when it is extreme, as in terror, with its consequent mental paralysis – but as with all things human, there are infinite gradations – from the severe to the minor to the everyday. They merge into one another, and can become quite difficult to distinguish. Indeed after a while, the only point in trying to tell these various bits apart is when it makes a practical difference.

So we look around our world, and we draw a tentative prediction about it. This may be trivial – is it going to rain today? Or more profound – is there a God who will look after my every step? Now each of these thoughts carries an emotion with it. There is no such thing as an emotionless thought or a thoughtless emotion i.e. a thought without emotion – here's another of those 'mergings' which though often useful in practice, become intolerably complex in theory. Emotions are what move thought about. Thoughts follow a certain logic for a limited distance, but they arise, 'become motivated' by emotion. So it makes sense to say that every emotion moves a thought, from which it follows that no thought can exist unless it has its mover, its emotion in tow, or the other way around. The key to mental stability is to balance these two, to keep them in harmony. Thus the thoughts that occur to you, will be born to you on a bed of harmonious emotions – and when they are not, then you can think through steps to ensure that they henceforth do.

With all this fluidity, flux and potential chaos around, small wonder the human mind clings to apparent fixity. A thought becomes coloured in a deeper hue, it seems to be of the royal purple, it rises above the normal hubbub – and hey presto you have an unsinkable belief, which degrades ever so gently into a dogma. On this reading therefore, a dogma is just a thought, a notion, an idea or conception that has taken on a patina of permanence. And, as you might come to expect, there is only one main emotion that leads to such unhealthy inflexibility, and that is fear.

So every dogma arises first from fear. Fear of uncertainty, fear of the enormous complexity, nay the chaos of the inanimate world, fear of unreliability, fear of untrustworthiness, fear of deceit – and so on. So you find ordinary men and women latching onto the first apparently reliable tenets they were served with when young, and they cling to them through thick and thin, even when so much evidence piles up to show they are no longer realistic or helpful.

The truth is – there are no fixities out there. The whole inanimate cosmos is woven from genuine pure chaos. But there is a way through – there are human beings out there who live in the same chaotic world – but who, by the simple fact of being alive, can do something about it. They can create an area of relative stability. They can build a small patch of peace. But to do that, they have first to rinse out all the bits of fear which seem to breed ubiquitously, like so many bacteria.

denial re-visited

How can I write a book replete with such robust views and so many categoric statements, while simultaneously decrying dogma? The disadvantages of dogma are all too easy to spot – in other people. The rigidities, the ludicrous deductions, the ever widening gap between them and reality – these cannot stay hidden for ever. But what happens all too often, is that those who decry yesterday's dogma hasten to replace it with a more recent model, one they have just cooked up today. It may take a generation or more, to catch on to the cracks that then appear in that one, whence a new one is offered up to replace it. The military together with certain prime ministers perennially insist on re-fighting the war before last.

Again those who throw away all dogmas, who espouse nihilism, anarchy and shapelessness are, like so many of the early existentialists, rather too uncomfortable to live with for long. However there is a thin pathway between. I have labelled it Nexistentialism. To deal effectively with what happens next, which is something all of us do all day, every day – it's what our minds are for – you need to have an accurate picture of what's happening now. This goes under the rubric 'Truth'. This can never be 100%, but the nearer it gets, the truer it is.

What our minds are doing is penetrating the fog of circumstances and agencies impinging on our present, latching onto those that seem cardinal, and then acting as if they were. So, if you like, we make a short term dogma of these assessments, put our weight upon it, and then ditch it when it proves out of date, as it inevitably will. If you insist, you can therefore have short term and long term dogmas. I wouldn't object too strongly, provided you are prepared to adjust all of them, when realities change.

If I might attempt to curry a little favour with my erstwhile medical colleagues – I would stoutly declare that this is a precise description of what happens in clinical medicine. It is in essence, the clinical approach – where 'clinic' comes from the Greek word for 'bed', and it implies you have to do what you can with what you've got at the material time at the bedside. Sir William Osler had a wonderful metaphor for it, along the lines that – *to study patients without reading books is to go to sea without charts – but to study books without seeing patients, is never to go to sea at all*. My rendition of the same sentiment is – you need to know the text book well enough, to know that what's in front of you, isn't in it.

So there is a pedigree for Nexistentialism. What you do next depends on what you think is happening now, and what you understood to have happened before. The future, after all, is the moment that's just about to arrive. When it does, it becomes the present, which in turn and just as mysteriously, solidifies into the past. I like to call this the Existential Moment. No wonder this is difficult to capture in scientific theories. No wonder there is enormous controversy about whether this or that is an Art or a Science. I would like to suggest that all of it is – reality. If you ask an engineer to build a bridge, or a doctor to handle an epidemic, or a teacher to dispel ignorance, or an economist to promote wealth – then you are asking them to assess the best available practice, the most accurate picture of what is now happening, from which the optimum way forwards is selected. Dogmas can dog progress at any of these three points – but the proof of the recipes lies in the wholesomeness of the outcomes. Every time. Without exception. Bar none.

Which brings us neatly back to denial again. For with denial we have a yesterday's 'truth' that has become cemented in so deep, it is inconceivable that it should be changed, or even very closely broached. And it is cemented there by fear. Any non-fleeting thought that persists longer than is warranted by changed circumstances is best regarded first as a dogma, and then, if it is especially deep and especially obdurate, as a buried or obsolete terror.

As before, denial works by scaring off further reflection or re-consideration of the thought in question. What cannot be thought about, cannot be re-cast, cannot be re-thought, and cannot therefore be correlated with what is actually happening now – this we label 'denied'. Reality is relegated to what you thought before – irregardless of how much reality itself has actually changed, as change it invariably does. Here be deep dogmas indeed.

So there is a profound link between dogmas and denials. In fact, it might simplify things to say that the remedy for mental illhealth is to find the obsolete dogmas which infest the sufferers' minds, and assist in evicting them. And this is precisely what happens during Emotional Education, or Emotion Support. What you need to do is provide enough security, enough trustworthiness to hold the fear at bay long enough for the sufferer to bring their mental furniture up to date. It may sound long winded in verbal description – but in practice it is remarkably simple – not necessarily easy, but quite essentially simple.

A further point needs making here. Every instance of emotional distress arises from a dogma peculiar to that person. The symptoms may vary even more widely than those recorded in the DSM-IV. But the deeper origin is always the same – a dogma laid down when circumstances were more threatening, and which can only be extirpated when circumstances become favourable. The point to make is that every child growing up experiences life differently. The dogmas they lay down vary infinitely depending on what happens to them individually, and how they see or react to that. Every child in effect develops different ways of handling things when they go wrong. Some of these ways are more flexible than others – those least flexible last longer. It would be dogmatic to say, for instance, that every emotional distress arises from precisely the same event – so those trying to assist must therefore retain a remarkable degree of flexibility, as will be discussed further below.

The Healing Hand Of Kindness

So having swept away all dogma, or at least kept all those we have to on a very short lease, what are we left with? What are the Universals of the human mind, Universal because you are going to find them in every instance of mind that comes your way. The less savoury aspects have already been much discussed – here the more positive features come to the fore.

Well, the purpose of the guided tour of the human mind which opened this chapter was to highlight those aspects every human holds in common with every other. Thus we can all think, we can all create new notions – some more than others, but such creativity is available to all. It goes with the mechanism of thinking things through, of reflecting on what to do next. Incidentally for those readers who pondered the accuracy of the phrase "fear impedes rational thought – it's the only thing that can" – it should be stressed that thought occurring in any awake mind tends to be rational – the irrational arises solely from operating obsolete dogmas, 'truths' which held true in the past but not anymore. And the only reason a mind tolerates such anachronisms is because they are too fearful to be brought up to date – the housekeeping role of intent is put on hold because of fear.

So human universals are a tendency to dogma which must be recognised and resisted – and a need for trust, which must be acknowledged and sustained. And the universal remedy for obsolete fear is emotional support, trustworthy emotional support. The Healing Hand of Kindness is Robert Whitaker's term and it's very apt. He also points out that when this was applied in the past, notably in the early 1800s, it produced a better rate of cure of the psychoses than any other 'treatment' deployed since – which includes all psychiatric drugs currently manufactured (and especially those).

The Healing Hand of Kindness is like broad spectrum antibiotics used to be – they would reliably clear bacterial infections as never before. Or like blood of the group AB negative, which is regarded as a 'universal donor' in that it can be given to all other blood groupings. Since all humans are born sociable, all respond to the Healing Hand of Kindness, which when appropriately applied, with sufficient trustworthiness, is universally therapeutic. Why should it be a puzzle that being kind, considerate and responsive helps human beings who suffer emotional distress? Why should one have to point it out? When will it become obligatory? It is universal truth that until it does our recovery rates from emotional distress will remain low. But when Kindness finally wins, these rates will rise, and with the exorcism of denial, can go on rising to 100%.

Dr Peter Breggin's support and inspiration

Dr Peter Breggin is a well known pioneer for better psychiatry, active in the United States since the late 1960s. He has written widely, and has been a positive inspiration to me personally. As will be apparent from the following paragraphs, there is no way this book would even have started without his significant support.

The part played by Robert Whitaker has already been mentioned. But there is little doubt that without Dr Breggin, it would not have seen the light of day. It's a very curious thing, but the professional code of conduct instilled in all medical students from day one, is hard to resist. I have tried to depict its impact in earlier chapters. It is one of the reasons psychiatric reform is so tardy. So when the opportunity falls to me to stand up for what my profession does not believe, the first response is dalliance and deferral – couldn't someone else take up the baton? The fallout will be horrendous, the brick-bats painful, the chances of success equivocal at best – so why not go for a comfortable retirement? You would scarcely credit the mud that has already been heaped upon me in the past – so it is as well to have no illusions about the intensity of psychiatric rage, both by psychiatrists and their clientele.

Dr Breggin however welcomed me into his home and, if I may say so, into his heart. I admit that when we first spent time together, we circled each other rather as porcupines do – after all, psychiatrists roused can be spiky indeed. But we persevered. I discovered a man who had been battling the same forces of psychiatric nihilism as I had, over the same 40 years, and, I am happy to record, with rather more success. Even while we were staying with him and his wife, he was called away on a court case concerning the damage done by Ritalin, which was settled for $1,500,000. His expertise in the court room is justifiably renowned.

In 1972 he won a legal battle in the southern USA regarding the use of brain damaging leucotomies or lobotomies then being performed on young black children. This erected a legal barrier to any further such malign surgery in that country. Marvellous. My own humiliating failure to build a similar legal obstacle to further use of Electro Convulsive Treatment (ECT), mentioned earlier, stands in marked contrast. I have a deep respect for what he has done, and I salute his talents and his abilities in doing it.

The organisation he founded, the International Center for the Study of Psychiatric and Psychology, runs annual conferences in the United States, which people attend to breathe the fresh air of psychiatric realism. At the last, in October 2005, Dr Grace Jackson, author of *'Rethinking Psychiatric Drugs : A Guide for Informed Consent'* horrified us with scientific data proving that psychiatric drugs cause brain cell death – surely if this was widely known as it should be, then public intervention would be more pressing.

The immediate impulse for this present book came from the idea of a public debate which I have long wished for, to shine the harsh light of publicity into this dark corner of unsavoury psychiatric practice. Now a debate requires a title or a motion – and the first one to come up was, "Psychiatric drugs do more harm than good". Dr Peter Breggin welcomed this warmly. Brainstorming this with my wife, and tying it in with the way Ralph Nader raised public awareness, in the 1960s when campaigning against the automobile industry – Ralph Nader's book *Unsafe At Any Speed* came to mind. Only a little adaptation was needed to bring up the title *Unsafe At Any Dose.* Dr Breggin was even warmer in his enthusiasm for this one. The title for the book followed smoothly, which then fired my enthusiasm to write it.

I would protest my views on psychiatry in any context, as robustly as the next man or woman. But inviting your own psychiatric colleagues to dispense with their time honoured practices, and in particular their cosy, comfortable concretisms is more challenging than you might think. It is not something you rush into. After all, I too have faced the indecisions, the woolly indeterminate nature of mental distress, the compelling need to 'do something' because all around are looking to you to solve the problem, ease the mental pains, if not cure the disease.

And I do not hold it against my psychiatric colleagues that they did not at first recognise the fundamental role that obsolete terror plays – what I do now castigate them for is a closed unwillingness to listen, not only to their patients, but to the objective scientific evidence, now abundantly available for everyone else to read. In this, I distinguish between DSM-psychiatrists, and those confident enough and supported enough to disregard the inhumane injunctions that that unhappy bible compels. It is in this regard that Dr Peter Breggin's overt, and warm support for this venture finally tipped me into putting it all down on paper, and sending it off to the printers. Thank you Peter, from the bottom of my heart.

micro-Darwinism

Charles Darwin was a remarkable man. At considerable personal cost he confronted the religious dogmas of his day, and provided frail but steady schemata for stringing together a rethinking of most of the biosphere. Of course he acknowledged there were 'missing links' in his theory – generally between apes and man. In fact, despite its brilliance his theory turns out to be a tissue of missing links, rather like the schoolboy's definition of a net – a lot of holes tied together with string.

Creationism has recently shown an ugly recrudescence – indicating a desire to return to dogmas commonplace several millennia before the Old Testament. But there is another aspect of living organisms which Darwin did not address, and which passes most Neo-Darwinists by. And that is an aspect of evolution which we each of us experience often enough, a type of micro-evolution, something difficult to describe but essentially rather miraculous.

At this point, the discussion needs assistance from that thread regularly offered in earlier chapters to convey a line of reasoning more closely akin to the experience of the reader. Rather than pains in the leg, here we call upon the services of a wooden leg. Suppose part of your lower limb had been amputated, and replaced with an artificial contraption, for simplicities sake let's say it was a wooden leg.

What difference would this make? Well first of all you'd have to learn to operate it, to trust it to bear your weight, go where you wanted it to go, and so forth. But watch what happens. Say you bump it, bruise it, or even cut it inadvertently on some sharp edge. A gash appears on the leg. And it stays there. It does not go away. You have then to repair it, repaint it, replace it or otherwise intervene to repair the damage. This is not at all remarkable – all such gadgets go out of kilter from time to time, and need constant vigilance and intervention to maintain them in the serviceable condition we would wish them to be in.

The remarkable thing is that this is precisely what you did not need to do with your leg when it was healthy. The normal leg submits to bumps, bruises, cuts and even factures – and it heals itself. How does it do this? Somehow it takes over the intervention that non-living legs require, and repairs itself on its own initiative, using its own powers of organisation, its own anti-entropy facility.

So what are you going to call this? Or are you going to conclude that, since it does not fit it with any convenient scientific theory, certainly not Darwinism as it was – that it should remain outside our consideration altogether? Have a care here – the temptation to say that because we cannot understand something that therefore it isn't happening, may lead to missing the point of the whole exercise, the whole escape hatch. Because there's no theory, not even the wisp of a suggestion of a theory – does this mean we should shut the whole thing in the cupboard, and leave it strictly alone? I rather hope not, since it underpins the whole of the philosophy proffered in this book.

I freely admit again, I have no idea what intent is – but I know for an absolute certainty that it is quite crucial for mental health. Everyone with the least emotional distress would warmly welcome help to pull themselves together, provided it was offered in a non-parental, trustworthy way. Now the thing that does the 'pulling together' is exactly the same as the thing that does the housekeeping mentioned above – viz intent.

Again, I don't need to know what intent is – just how to facilitate it in others, and indeed in myself. The situation is exactly the same with any surgeon. None of them has the least idea what 'healing' actually is, or how it comes about. But all of them now know that infections make it worse, if not impossible – a situation that did not obtain in Victorian times. Ignorance of micro-organisms has already been compared with ignorance of fear – which is a dogma too many psychiatrists hold with today.

Healing of a cut or an incision is peculiarly apt here – it used to be called 'healing by first intention', i.e. before infection set in. Here 'intention' is being correctly used. Somehow there is a link between a leg or a cut healing itself, and a mind doing the same – both partake in that rather miraculous process which we are currently calling 'intent'. There is a decided similarity in what happens to the cut leg and to the broken mind, but does not happen to the wooden leg. You can decide what you want to call it – I call it micro-intent. You can of course continue to exclude it from your conversations, even from your mind – but I suggest that if you do so, you would miss out something rather remarkable, and certainly something indispensable if you are interested in peace of mind.

And the exoticism does not end there. Not only do we have intent – at least we do in my experience – but we also have micro-intent, our legs, indeed our body generally evolves to a healthier state once the main pathology is eased. Certainly our minds do, once our 'denials' are identified and our fears slaked so that our denying and our dogmas evaporate. But if our skin evolves back to where it was before it was cut – thus defying the physical law of entropy – what about the transitions that took place on an evolutionary scale? The growing of legs from fins in the first place?

The orthodox dogma is genetic mutation – genes are supposed to be damaged by cosmic rays and other noxious agents, which produces a whole range of different and essentially random changes only some of which survive, through a 'survival of the fittest' test. Random? Give me strength. When cells do evolve randomly, we call them cancerous. There is nothing random about my healed leg, nor indeed about my healed mind. Whoever conjured up the gene as an idol to be worshipped has a lot to answer for. Genes can hide more dogmas than you can shake a stick at, a helical stick at that.

micro-Darwinism

For my money, I like to think that the process which preserves my body from entropical decay is exactly that which allowed my fishy forebears to gradually evolve into the wonderful patterns we see today. For want of a reliable 'definable' lexicon, we risk missing the really remarkable, almost miraculous aspect of living organisms. You do not have to believe in God, or Science, or Darwin, or Cosmic Radiation, or Blind Faith, or in anything else that you can't see and I can – you just have to open your eyes to what happens when you cut your finger. If you insist on waiting for cosmic rays to randomly mutate the genes in your skin, then don't bother asking me for a sticking plaster.

I have little doubt that this idea of micro-intent, of Darwinism on a micro-cellular scale will receive rough treatment. I am even anticipating it being allied with witchcraft, whereby things happen as a result of mumbo jumbo, and esoteric ingredients. I rebut that last charge, on the grounds that I know exactly what is happening – provided you don't push me too deep. I know that keeping a wound clean and dry promotes healing, that clarting it with wet lotions and ointments tends to delay matters. I do not call on the moon to assist this process, nor yet on some fanciful ray nor astrological device – I call on the healthy skin to do what it does naturally – as all living things do – to organise itself, resist entropy and within well known limits – get well.

It is likely that some eyebrows will rise on finding Darwin included in a book seeking to rekindle psychiatry. But Darwin featured in the last part of *Emotional Health*, and he does so here for the same reason. There are many mysteries out there that we shall never unpick – but there others nearer to home that we need to familiarise ourselves with, if we wish to do better than witch-doctoring. And to this end I propose to enlist the entire medical profession to my aid, despite the brickbats lobbed recently in its direction. Ask any doctor you wish, how skin heals. Ask any doctor you know to define what pain is. Ask any doctor, anywhere, if he or she would prefer to exclude considerations of these ultimately mysterious items, on the ground that there was no satisfactory way of measuring them, or of defining them, or even of describing them in any scientific, objective or repeatable manner. Despite these gaping holes in medical knowledge, these are two of a whole range of items which the entire medical profession will never ever give up. All I am asking them, and indeed you to do, is add 'intent' and parts of 'micro-intent' to that list – which many of them already do. For without applying intent, there can be no mental housekeeping, no mental stability, no healing of grievous emotional distress, and certainly by a wide margin, no possibility of peace of mind.

erasing psychiatric dogmas.

The dogmas listed in the first chapter now need to be reviewed in the light of the foregoing. Fear is far and away the most significant emotion. Indeed there is no doubt that if you were permitted to deal with only one emotion, then this would be the one to choose. You might think of it as vague, woolly, indefinable or totally subjective and introspective. But this is not how the emotional sufferer sees it, nor how they will describe it to you, if you provide the appropriately supportive and encouraging setting for them to do so.

Exactly the same woolliness and vagueness applies to pain – yet so invaluable is it in medical practice, that you never ever hear complaints about it on this score. Nor ever will. It is the master compass by which a good clinician will diagnose your ailments; the infallible guide to the underlying pathology. It is the central reason why Sir William Osler's axiom is so pertinent to good clinical practice – listen to the patient, s/he is telling you about the pain. How the pain came, where it spreads to, what makes it worse, what better – all these are gold dust in the clinician's endeavours to make sense of what ails you. A good history of pain is worth its weight in gold, or at least in life saving ability. No practising clinician would gainsay this – indeed I would ask everyone of them, sight unseen, to vouch for it 100%

If a practising clinician, even an experienced medical editor, heard that pain was being disparaged, excluded, by-passed because it was vague and woolly – there would be an immediate and negative reaction. Such a notion would be counter to the entire spirit of clinical medicine. To emphasise the point, as a GP, when dealing with abdominal pain I had, painfully, to withhold the morphine. Had I killed the pain, the surgeon would have been 'blind' to the underlying pathology, and pain would not have been the only thing to die that day.

In this context too, it is clear that any psychiatric drug does just what the morphine would have done in general practice – it befuddles the fear, making it harder to unpick, to dig up the roots and to trace it back to its origins. One day the psychiatric profession will appreciate this profoundly significant medical point. The patients in general practice would plead with me to dull the pain, they put as much pressure on me as they reasonably could, even perhaps regarding me as somewhat callous. But I have removed 30 appendices, I know what a challenge 'the acute abdomen' can represent, so I manfully resisted. In the case of psychiatry, the sufferers are often even more insistent, they self-medicate wherever they can, they do not believe that any other relief is available for their fears. Part of their education is showing them that there is, and that a permanent cure is available to all those who work for it. A 'live' illustration of how this works out in practice follows in the next three chapters.

Fear plays exactly the same role in mental health as pain does in physical health. The additional difficulty, as mentioned, is that the sufferer tries to keep it from him or herself, by 'denying' it, so as to reduce it to manageable proportions. This does not make the practice of psychiatry any easier. Indeed it allows psychiatric dogma to flourish, without active protestations from the sufferers. They don't believe there is any answer to their fears anyway, other than keeping them well hidden, so why wave them about? If the doctor shows no interest in them either, then this at least saves them the trouble of turning over the hot coals at the backs of the mind, which might well prove damaging – certainly they give every indication of so being.

However the analogy with pain is tighter still. Where the fear came from, what it stops you doing now, who or what eases it – all these are again gold dust, to understanding the roots of the emotional distress. There is an additional bonus. When the roots of the fear are uncovered, then the sufferer is encouraged to laugh at their origin. This serves both to undo the denial, and cures the symptoms at the same time – a double bonus all round.

The dogma that entails ignoring the mind because you cannot see it, must surely go by the board. Every emotional sufferer freely testifies to its existence – only by persistently ignoring what their patients say, can DSM-psychiatrists proceed as if it did not.

Many sufferers, including Lenny, who appears next, are comfortable with the analogy with computer programming. They have been mis-programmed – Lenny goes to far as to say he has been brainwashed into fear – he sees what happened to him as a type of brainwashing. It should be made clear that this is not to regard the human mind as in any way like a robot or a digital computer. The topic is discussed in *Emotional Health.*

The reality is that only humans have the creativity, the ability to create something de novo, a facility indispensable to programming inert solid state computers. But what happens too often, is that the data – the dogmas that a growing child absorbs willy-nilly from his or her environment – this is what that person utilises in adult life. Where this becomes misshapen, then it needs straightening before the ill-consequences go away. But go away they can. And though typed dialogue can never have the same impact as watching a video, or participating in person – this is what we are confined to so far, and to this we now turn.

5) EMOTION SUPPORT for Lenny

On Monday 1st July 1991, I started work in Parkhurst Prison, at that time a maximum security prison on the Isle of Wight. This was the flagship of the prison system, with a young, go-ahead governor at the helm. I would never have planned to work there, having resolved some three decades earlier not to work in large institutions ever again, since they were invariably toxic. However, serendipity came to my rescue. John Marriott had recently been promoted to be governor there, and via a strong family connection had invited me to join the staff, as Consultant Psychiatrist to the Special Unit. This unit was modelled on the Special Unit in Barlinnie Prison in Scotland, though there were repeated disclaimers against this link. Essentially it was for prisoners too violent for Broadmoor, the maximum security hospital in the south of England.

I did not go into Parkhurst empty handed. I had developed in general practice, a model regarding the long term effects of childhood trauma, and I was anxious to apply this to as wide a range of clinical problems as I could. Had I taken Freud's model, unreconstructed, with me then I would have earned myself a gruesome fate. As my work progressed, it became ever clearer that these prisoners, all lifers, virtually all murderers – had killed or attacked a figment derived directly from their childhood. Generally this turned out to be a parent, oftentimes an abuser.

Thus had I followed Freud's advice and invited them to transfer their parental feelings onto me – essentially the Freudian 'transference' – I would have been asking for trouble, possibly lethal trouble. As it was, three murderers threatened to kill me, because I had trespassed too abruptly and too soon on to their obsolete terrors, and their remedy was to stop me going any further, by stopping me altogether, a method they had used before.

The actual technique – what to say, and when to say it – is unlikely to be easily conveyed by reading printed words from a paper page. The human mind is so flexible fluid and dynamic that those who wish to follow its cogitations must maintain a high level of alertness, flexibility and fluidity themselves – hard to convey in fixed print. What these pages are intended to do, is to give some idea of how denial works, where fear can lead you, and what sort of interventions work for the best. Another key point is to demonstrate that these are not normal conversations. I take liberties with the topic – I abruptly stop one theme, and start another. This may seem rude – but it is done with the sufferer's consent. It is also quite essential, since unless I can find areas where my view of reality differs from that stored in the mind of the other, then there would be little point to the whole procedure in the first place.

Further, I need to encourage the conversation into places that the other does not want to go – no point chuntering on, covering ground we both agree with. The key is to find those points of difference, to bring them to the surface, and allow the sufferer thereby to bring them up to date – all within a context of complete trust and support. I have shown the video of this session countless times – it is such a clear demonstration of the issues involved. It shows how honest Lenny is being – he admits the humiliating truth that part of him is still stuck in childhood where he is still vulnerable to "batterings". This is so clearly not the case in today's reality – but it needs teasing out slowly so that he can see this for himself.

Fear makes its appearance early on, it leads to "embedding" or being stuck. And it also leads to not having grown up. The key is to find precepts, or dogmas if you will, that are based on these childhood realities, and which are absurd in today's reality. We needed to talk about being an adult, and we needed to examine quite what Lenny could do with this powerful word, in the context in which his mother could hear him. Almost immediately, I am contrasting what today's reality should be telling him – e.g. "You're a big lad," with what his fears are telling him. "Part of you is still there" i.e. still in childhood. The answer to "Could you tell her you're an adult?" should be a resounding "Yes". But it isn't – and thereby hangs the tale.

VIDEO INTERVIEW BETWEEN DR JOHNSON AND A PRISONER ON 'C' WING PARKHURST 11th September 1991

B: How would you describe to someone who doesn't know anything about it what questions I am asking you, and what we are doing.

L: Well it's about my Mother, how she used to batter me when was a kid.

B: What effect did this have on you?

L: Well it made me frightened.

B: Did it?

L: Yes.

B: What's happened to the fear?

L: It's embedded.

B: It's still there is it?

L: Yes.

B: It doesn't help you does it?

L: No.

B: What effect does this embedded fear have?

L: It's made me violent.

B: Did it?

L: Yes.

B: How does that work?

L: I don't know.

B: Why does embedded fear make you violent?

L: Well she used violence on me all the time and I grew up to violence didn't I? Do you know what I mean?

B: But you're a big lad and you're an adult, so why are you still frightened of your Mother? . . . . It's still there isn't it?

L: I'm still there, yes.

B: So why hasn't it changed? Why is it still there, do you think?

L: Well, it's all part of growing up, isn't it?

B: Part of you hasn't, has it?

L: Yes.

B: Part of you is still stuck there, isn't it?

L: Yes.

B: Because we talked about that this morning didn't we?

L: Yes.

B: Being an adult. Can you tell her you're an adult?

L: Yes, I could try.

"Yes, I could try," shows where the trouble lies. Either Lenny is an adult, and should be able to tell everybody effortlessly – or he is not, in which case then something very peculiar is going on. Well to everyone else it is obvious he is an adult – to himself, when his mother is in the vicinity, the question is in doubt, the outcome precarious.

Lenny catches on quickly. He agrees, when asked to comment on this handicap, that it is 'surprising' – indeed he calls it 'very surprising', which shows just how relaxed he is, how confident that I am there to support him, and that he has well learnt the lesson that it will pay him to let me press him on these painful points. It also shows me where the fault line is. I am always anticipating a fault line – but since every child grows up differently – only the person in front of you knows precisely where it is. And since they have always dealt with this overwhelming problem by denying it, it takes a lot of courage and trust on their part for them to vary this defence routine now. It also requires a verbal spanner – that is to say, a form of words which carries weight with the sufferer. In this case, that spanner is clearly to do with stating clearly, and without fear "Hello mother, I'm an adult".

When Lenny agrees he would find it difficult to say this, I move quickly to link this difficulty with the master emotion – fear. And also to the fact that in today's world he has no need to be afraid. To emphasise the issue, I invite him to compare his body size with that of his mother – there's no contest. Except there obviously is a contest still going on in his mind. This is a clear demonstration of an earlier childhood dogma "I'm smaller than Mum", which is so obviously out of date – obvious to everyone else but not, so far, to Lenny.

The fear, like all such fear, is of being damaged by a destructive parent. Lenny is quick to see that it would be 'nice' to be able to disagree with his mother, and that if and when he could do this, he could "get on with my own life". The latter clearly being something he has not so far been able to do.

B: Would you find it difficult?

L: Yes.

B: You would, wouldn't you?

L: Yes.

B: Do you find that surprising, that you find it difficult to tell your mother you're an adult?

L: Yes. Very surprising.

B: It is isn't it. So what will stop you? Say your mother was sitting over there, what would you say to her?

L: I'd say "Mother you can't hit me any more. I am an adult."

B: And you believe that?

L: Yes, partly. [both laugh]

B: You partly believe it and partly don't?

L: Yes. I don't know whether I could say it to her or not.

B: What would stop you?

L: Fear.

B: Fear of what? What is she going to do?

L: Well she might get up and clout me.

B: Might she?

L: She might.

B: How old is she?

L: 85.

B: And she is going to do you an injury is she?

L: Oh she's still lively.

B: 85. How big is she?

L: 5 feet 2 inches. [158 cms]

B: And how big are you?

L: 6 feet 3□ inches. [192 cms]

B: It doesn't sound much of a match does it?

L: No, but you can't hit a woman can you?

B: You can't disagree with your Mother, let alone hit her can you?

L: No.

B: Do you need to be able to disagree with her?

L: It would be nice to, wouldn't it?

B: Would it? What advantage to you is disagreeing with your Mother?

L: Well, I could get on with my own life.

B: Could you?

L: Yes.

It is then instructive to ask what he would do, had he the confidence to do it. What would he actually want to say? And what difference would this make to him?

He reverts directly to the "batterings" – these were the reason he left home. Why the present government hesitates so long to outlaw smacking is hard to follow – especially when one continually hears stories such as this one, with its profoundly damaging consequences. Again, rather than go too far down memory lane, I bring the theme back to fear - the residual fear of his mother.

Next there is a bit of a hiatus in the conversation, so I pull out what we were discussing earlier that day. The word "programming" was mentioned there, and so I remind Lenny of this. He responds right on cue and links it quite explicitly with fear of his mother.

Not only is he still afraid, but his picture of himself in his mind, is that he remains smaller than her. So often this discrepancy in size is solidly fixed in the sufferer's mind even when, as here, the difference in reality is not minor, it is gross. Infantile views are invariably a long way removed from today's adult reality – but the difficulty of bringing these two together in the same mind, is often a challenge. Of course, the smallest hint that you are not being fully supportive, that you might be making fun of this irrationality, or 'stupidity', leads to the mind of the sufferer clanging tightly shut, with a finality that can be awesome.

Following the hiatus, I then relentlessly steer the conversation back to the sore point, the painful issue – are you going to tell her? He mutters. So I grasp the point robustly, and wave it under his nose. Give him credit, he rises to the challenge – feels out his new support from me, and launches into an area of his mental world he has never dared venture into before. I'm exploring what role I'm playing too. While he is still looking for the word, I jump in with 'moral support'. But power is much nearer the mark – I am empowering him to pull himself together – which of course I'm delighted to be able to do.

B: What would you tell her?
L: I'd say leave me alone.
B: Get out of my life?
L: That's why I left home.
B: Why did you leave home?
L: Because I couldn't put up with her batterings any more.
B: You couldn't, could you?
L: No.
B: How old were you when you left home?
L: Oh don't forget I was in Approved School so I left when I was 13 and I didn't go back home. Oh I'm a liar, I did go back home, I did, but it was getting on my nerves, all the shouting and bawling.
B: And even at that time you were still afraid of your Mother weren't you?
L: Oh yes.
B: You said this morning you were programmed. What was the programme?
L: Programmed to be afraid of my mother.
B: You were, weren't you?
L: Yes.
B: Also programmed to be smaller than her.
L: Yes, she thinks I am still in shorts.
B: She does, doesn't she?
L: She does.
B: So are you going to tell her? . . . . . I beg your pardon?
     Are you going to tell her?
L: If she was here now. [with rising tone of voice]
B: Yes.
L: If she was here now - and if you was here.
B: Right.
L: "Mother you can't touch me I'm an adult." I would, I would say that.
B: You would?
L: Yes.
B: That's because I'm here?
L: That's because you're here.
B: What role do I play? How am I helping you to do that?
L: Well, you are giving me . . . .
B: Moral support?

101

As always, it is essential to bring matters back to today's reality. There is nothing special about me – I am not waving a magic wand that is not available to Lenny. I do not have any magical power which enables me to work special miracles. All I am doing is bringing strength to an area in Lenny's mental world where I am not afraid of what we might find, and he is.

I also need to emphasise that the anger and fear that Lenny feels for his mother is irrational, that is – it's obsolete, and needs to be seen as that, so that it can evaporate harmlessly. When I press him on linking his violence to the fear of his mother, he takes on something of a weary tone, as if explaining to a simpleton. I can tolerate this, and I hang on, touching back all the time to the obsolete fear, or indeed terror of his mother.

"Have you never heard of this before?" – he's getting quite exasperated with me at this stage. Even going so far as to ask "Do you get the point?" Can you imagine many long term prisoners taking this sort of liberty with their Consultant Psychiatrist who writes their reports and might organise impromptu transfers virtually anywhere? I should correct the above – I do not only tolerate this – it is a feather in my cap. I am just the man next door, I am on exactly the same level as he is – he is pointing things out to me, just as he would to a rather dim yokel down the road. What a compliment to a man in my position! What a privilege to be able to join Lenny at a level he can recognise, so that he can accept the strength and courage I bring to an area where he has none, or did have none, to date.

The other point to emphasise is that he is now beginning to think things through for the first time. He is just starting to connect his outbursts, his irrationality to someone else. Always before it was down to him – the world told him he was scum, and he saw no reason to disbelieve them. Here he is re-evaluating the most significant emotional items in his life. What a privilege to be there assisting him in doing this. And what a reward to see him blossoming emotionally – it's worth a few brick-bats from him, to see this regeneration, this bursting forth anew. A privilege indeed.

L:.   . . . . power.

L: Yes.

B: I am aren't I?

L: Yes.

B: After a while you can do it for yourself, without me can't you?

L: Oh, of course, yes.

B: But at the moment you need my support.

L: Yes.

B: Which I am very happy to give you because I believe you are an adult and I believe she should be told. [Both laugh] That's right isn't it?

L: Yes.

B: Now could you tell me something about your violence and how that relates to fear of your Mother, if it does.

L: I've been pushed around and pushed around and pushed around that much, that I just couldn't take any more when this lad started, and I just went too far.

B: How does that relate to your Mother?

L: Well, it's bound to isn't it?

B: Go on then.

L: She used violence on me and I couldn't do anything back.

B: You couldn't do anything back.

L: No, and when he started giving me some lip . . .

B: Right.

L: I battered the hell out of him.

B: Yes.

[Here Lenny gives details of his crime which I've judged it better to omit]

B: So how is that violence related to fear of your Mother? How does that work?

L: Have you never heard of this before? If violence is shown to you time and time again, there comes a time in your life when you just snap, and I snapped.

B: Right.

L: Do you get the point?

These questions from me testify to my feeling my way here. I'm still learning the ropes. I am learning from Lenny, the first murderer I have been able to get this close to. I've never had anything to do with violence before, never had the opportunity to look deeper into its origins. And here, with Lenny, that's exactly what I'm doing.

Here I am testing out the model that the adult is stronger, as a direct result of shedding light into this previously forbidden area. I'm happy Lenny is getting stronger, but I'm completely taken aback by his declaration that he is getting angry. This is my first few months in prison – 11 weeks to be precise – and Lenny is sitting between me and the door.

So my query "Are you? With her?" has more desperation about it at this stage than would have been the case a year or two down the line, when I had learnt to 'read' violence and anger much more expertly.

I struggle a bit therefore to link the anger which has rather burst onto the scene, with the fear, which is my constant refrain, the theme which justifies my tampering with these explosive issues in men who are here, precisely because they have responded to such things violently.

I'm a bit on thin ice when I try to claim more confidence in his mother's inability to "batter" him ever again, than he has. He "knows that" too. He is still responding a little too warmly for comfort, so I take a firm grip and steer the conversation where I want it to go – back to my reliable refrain about his telling her he's an adult.

I'm more comfortable here. I'm on firmer ground. So I tighten it up a little. I invite him to look her straight in the eye and say it – something that was way out of reach to begin with. This is how you have to proceed – always a little bit further ahead, always pushing – but never too hard. He rises, so I promptly challenge him to do it – "Go on then" – a challenge we both gain from – me by cementing our relationship, he in confidence, as he notes.

B: I do.

L: So you can say it's down to her.

B: Because of the violence coming from her?

L: Yes because of the violence coming from her.

B: And what's your defence against the violence coming from her again?

L: No chance.

B: What are you going to do. How are you going to stop it?

L: I'm going to tell her.

B: What are you going to tell her?

L: That I'm an adult.

B: You like that don't you?

L: Yes.

B: You're getting stronger as you say it, aren't you?

L: Yes, I am.

B: You can feel yourself getting more confident.

L: I'm getting angry as well.

B: Are you? With her?

L: With her.

B: You are, aren't you? You see the anger. . . . .   I agree with you, the anger and violence can live together, but behind the anger is fear, because you feel that there is no defence against your Mother doing it again.

L: She'd never be able to do it again.

B: I know that.

L: *I* know that.

B: That's it.

L: I know that.

B: You also know you're an adult, don't you?

L: Yes.

B: And you can tell her that?

L: Yes. I can do.

B: At the moment with assistance from me. But in due course on your own.

L: On my own, yes.

B: That's right. Look her straight in the eye and say "look Ma I'm an adult". Can you do that?

L: Yes.

B: Go on then.

And I then move swiftly to cover the gaping hole which just now threatened to throw me off balance. I want to know what happened to the anger. And I want to know that Lenny knows what happened to it, so that he can ensure that he will be able to deal with it the same way, next time.

To my delight and relief, he responds splendidly. We can both see his anger calming down. So much more permanent than any number of superficial 'anger management' courses.

Lenny now responds enthusiastically to my query as to whether this is helping him. And as usual, I want to know how. What have I said, what questions helped most, how have I helped – all with the aim of helping better next time.

His answers are not quite as much to the point as I would wish. But they lead on to that well enough. All the time, I am bringing his rational self, his reasoning ability to bear upon his emotions. There is an explanation for them, there is a pattern beneath them that he needs to master and then enact. The denial needs bringing to the surface, so that he can see it for what it is, a childish defence, an infantile protection against a threat which was serious, but is now trivial, in exactly the same measure as to his physical size is now in relation to that of his mother.

I then move on to discuss the fear directly. And again, to my immense satisfaction that fear is now visibly reduced, and with it any tendency to violence, something which is always irrational and infantile. Lenny concedes that this fear was certainly big to start with – but is now shrinking to a more manageable size.

His mention of "to start with" prompts me ask how he initially reacted to my probing this area. He is direct and quite explicit - he thought I was way off target. This is a vital point – my 'version' of reality clashed strongly with his – had they not done so, we would have continued on our own parallel lines. The contrast was between what he expected – more of the same, and a severe wrench, i.e. an opportunity to grow up emotionally.

L: Look Ma, I am an adult. And you can't touch me ever again. I've grown up, I haven't still got shorts on.

B: Does that give you confidence?

L: Yes it does, saying it.

B: Does it calm your anger down?

L: Yes it does, yes.

B: Does it?

L: Yes it does.

B: It gives a way out for it, doesn't it?

L: Yes.

B: Because that's the reality.

L: Course it is, yes.

B: So is this helping you, would you say?

L: Yes, it is helping me.

B: How would you summarise your position and how have I been able to help you?

L: Well, nobody's ever bothered before. They've just asked a few questions and that's it - blah, blah, blah, thank you mam and all that rubbish. The psychologist doesn't do anything.

B: So what questions have I asked you? And what has been helpful?

L: Well, you have asked me what my home life was like. Why did I start getting into trouble.

B: You've got an explanation for that now, haven't you?

L: Yes.

B: Which you can work out for yourself now, as it were.

L: Yes, that's right.

B: You've done very well. So you will get rid of this fear in due course?

L: Yes, I will.

B: How big is it, this fear?

L: Not all that big now.

B: It was big before?

L: It was big, when you started.

B: Was it?

L: Yes.

B: What did you think when I first started questioning you in this area?

L: I thought you was a 'quack'. [Both laugh]

B: Did you believe what I was saying?

L: I did – but I wanted to shy away from the truth.

And then he mentions that magic word "truth". On the video, you can see that I am a bit slow to confirm his declaration – so he seeks more from me. I have not the least problem in assuring him that he has told the truth. The beauty of this process is that the nearer we both get to the truth, then the less infantile, the less irrational are his emotions going to be.

And here too is the central issue again. He has survived so far with these fearsome tensions in his head – by denial. And when he could sense that I was interested in searching through them, his immediate impulse was to run, to have nothing to do with me, by 'walking off', or rather more accurately, by running away.

This is a common enough response. Indeed denial itself can be thought of as a constant 'running away' – running away from an obsolete threat, which on being confronted is seen as disappearing in a puff of the past.

Clearly my remarks about his mother could have triggered his retreat. But mercifully for me, he stuck with it – he did not turn tail and run, which the size of his buried terrors could well have induced him to do. Lenny was the first to respond to this approach – the others, more severely damaged, took far longer. Had they all been of the prolonged variety, I might well have been shaken in my confidence, and 'walked away' too.

Again you can see that Lenny was not only responding to what I happened to suggest – he could see that he was responding to the "truth". Or as I would put it, to a more accurate version of reality than his buried terrors had previous allowed him. I see exactly the same pathology, the same 'lesion' in every psychiatric condition I come across. The mind is not running smoothly, because it has been thrown off balance by a savage fear. Once that fear can be eased or lifted, then the natural healing process can come into play, the mind shakes off its dross, and begins to blossom – what a privilege to participate in that, and watch it happen.

B: Did you?

L: But I told you the truth didn't I? . . .   I have told you the truth?

B: Certainly.

L: I could have said "Ah well I don't want nowt to do with it," and walked off, couldn't I?

B: Yes.

L: It's like coming up against a brick wall isn't it?

B: People do that.

L: Yes. They shouldn't do that.

B: So you were going to do that, to begin with?

L: I was going to do, yes.

B: What was wrong? What was going to make you do that?

L: It was upsetting me - the way you was going on about it.

B: Was it?

L: Yes.

B: What exactly upset you?

L: Against my Mother.

B: You didn't like that at all?

L: No.

B: That's right.

L: But I had to go with it because it was the truth.

B: Because what I think goes wrong is, because I frighten people by going at it too much to begin with. Is that what you think, would you agree that?

L: When you kept saying about the spanners.

B: You've got the old pliers and pincers didn't you?

L: Yes, that's true.

B: But you stuck with it, didn't you?

L: Yes I did, yes.

B: You did very well. But you fancied stopping it at the beginning did you?

L: Yes, I did.

B: Because it was getting a bit near the bone?

L: That's right yes. But it's the truth, isn't it? The truth's got to come out hasn't it?   And you were trying to help me, and I am helping you.

B: I'm sure you are. So when the truth comes out – what would you say the truth was, that's got to come out?

L: Well the truth's got to come out and say "Right I'm not scared of my Mother any more". I'm going to tell her outright, "I'm an adult,"

Again, I want Lenny to own the process, so I ask him to re-cast it in his own words, which he has no difficulty in doing. This has the added bonus that he strengthens himself by doing so. It is really rather wonderful to see the steady accumulation of adult responsibilities. He rehearses the novel phrase "I'm an adult", and watches what happens to his mental apparatus as he does so. He begins to acquire self-respect. This shows too in his last but one comment on the previous page, where he adds that while I've been "trying to help" him – he has been helping me – a sentiment I am especially happy to agree with.

For the first time he begins to take control – his mother should start "talking nice" and leave aside the shouting she normally does. What a wonderful picture. Here are the seeds of civilised society, which Lenny is now preparing to play his full part in supporting – something that was simply not available to him before, and which our myopic prison service keeps insisting will not be available to him for a long time, if ever.

Bear in mind that every high security prisoner such as Lenny was then, costs us in the order of £1,000,000 a decade, and the full folly of our current penal system becomes more obvious. Truly the present system is an exceedingly expensive way of making things a great deal worse. I thank my lucky stars that for a brief 5 year period I was able to inject a different element into the situation, and of course to learn a great deal while doing so.

Eight weeks later, on 11 November 1991, Lenny is a dab hand at the business. I press him to state what he would say if his mother came across to hit him in the here and now. He astonishes me by saying he wouldn't have to "say" anything, he'd merely hold her hand. There is no malice in this gesture, there is no residual hate or anger - merely an assertion that the time for "battering" is long past. Lenny is now in charge. He knows now what was destabilising him, then. There is no need for him to be violent any more – the roots of that violence have been well and truly cut – he now knows where they came from, and how to ensure they never take a hold of him again.

no joking about. And say look, I've grown up now, you have got to start talking nice, and all that. No shouting like you normally do. B: And no threatening to batter you like she does.

L: Yes, that's right.

B: So the fear of her will disappear.

L: Yes.

B: Can you see how your anger went down? A little earlier on you were saying that you were angry, but the anger went down when you understood where it was coming from.

L: That's true. Yes, it's very true.

B: And that's the secret isn't it?

L: Yes.

B: Magic. Anyway thanks for coming along. And let me just double check that you don't mind if I show this to different people.

L: No, I don't mind at all.

B: Thank you very much indeed.

L: All right Bob.

B: Thanks, see you.

L: See you.

11 NOVEMBER 1991 – extract –

L : . . . . . You can't hit your own mother. Whenever she battered me, I'd never dream of lifting a hand to hit her.   Even when I was 21, she slapped me across the face.   And me Dad came in. And I ran out of the house. And slammed the door, and then just went and got pissed.

B : And bottled it up

L: Yes

B: But now you would stop her, if she came to hit you?

L: There's no way she would hit me now

B: What would you say?

L: I wouldn't have to say anything -- if she went to slap me, I'd just hold her hand.   *[both laugh]*

B: Well you didn't have the confidence to do that before

L: If this had've happened years ago, where a doctor had taken an interest say when I was in my twenties and said what you'd said and we'd conquered it, and then I went to the house.   And say I came in late, and she said blah blah blah and she went to hit me,

He looks back to what might have happened "say when I was in my twenties", and regrets as I do that it didn't. The emphasis is mine, and remains from the hand outs of this script I used so often. I was remarkably fortunate to have Lenny in my first batch at Parkhurst Prison. He was strong and brave enough to pick up the challenge I offered him. Others took materially longer – and had I not had this initial encouragement, I could well have been seriously discouraged. The next man in line was still debating, some 8 months later, whether he should see his father as a tall, powerful man, or like a match stick he could break in two with his hands. It took me a long time to realise that this dilemma was directly related to the level of the trauma that the individual had experienced, and therefore to the strength of denial that was needed to cope.

I have to mention one individual there, let's call him Tony, who came to see me every week for almost two years. He 'knew' that his mother was bigger than him, had always been bigger than him and would always be that way. In terms of the actual sizes that he would offer – there was the 'fact' that he was 5 feet 8 inches (172 cms), and the 'fact' she was 4 feet 10 (147 cms) – but these 'facts' had no impact on his assessment of her capacity to do him harm. In exasperation on one occasion, I suggested we had her in the room, so that they could stand back to back, and so prove which was the taller. His response was loaded with significance – "If she's in this room, I'm out of the building." So here is the problem in a nutshell – the powers of persuasion have to be strong enough to overcome the terrors and the denial which accompanies them. It's a question of thresholds. Where the terror is smaller, and the power of persuasion greater – then the resolution is swifter – conversely where the situation is other, the resolution is delayed. But either way, this is the reliable path to mental health – and it is open to all.

I'd say mother you can't hit me love, I'm a grown up.   You can't do it.   You can kick me out of the house

B: Because it's your house

L: But you can't hit me -- don't try and hit me

B: But you've never said that up until the last month or two

L: Yes.   I've never had the confidence to say it

B :   That's right.

L: You're brain washed into fear. . . . . . . *[continued]*

There are many more hours of video tape, tracing the progress of this approach through more severe cases than this, and through milder ones.

I hope that the foregoing gives some indication of how denial works, and how by confronting the fear which drives it, it is possible to remove it 100%. The antidote for fear, as my earlier book *Emotional Health* describes, is abundant supplies of trustworthy support. This dialogue and the ones that follow are intended to show that in action. A fuller account would undoubtedly come from a careful presentation of clips from the video bank – and hopefully these will eventually emerge. Meanwhile, we turn now to a case I have never seen, have had no professional dealings with at all. All I know about her is that her name isn't Louise. Indeed this was conducted over the internet in a closed confidential chat room via email. Whatever else this shows, it clearly demonstrates the power and flexibility of this approach.

6) EMOTION SUPPORT for Louise

When the writing appeared on the wall in Parkhurst Prison, indicating for those prepared to look, that my work had not attracted sufficient support from the Home Office to prolong my stay there, I began to look around to see how else I could employ myself. Following my 22 years before the mast in general practice, I knew there were a number of 'thick wallet' patients who kept coming back to their GPs and for whom little on the GP's prescription pad would assist. I therefore opened a clinic for treating such referrals from general practitioners in the area. The response was electric, and my clinic flourished, until the local psychiatrists decreed it closed.

One of the referrals who challenged me long and hard was Dawn. She had one of the more serious manifestations of panic attacks, limiting her access even to walking down the street, let alone going into a shop. Her partner had to give up work to help her.

Dawn and I wrestled with her obsolete terrors. We went scuttling through many a diversion. I even had to invent a new device, which really rather surprised me – namely, I had to warn her **not** to think about her terrors between one week and the next. Normally I would happily give my customers 'homework' – "Upset Mum and I'm free", or "Back Off Dad," or something similar depending on the circumstances. The idea was that by reciting such phrases initially by rote, their truth would slowly percolate through, and today's reality would finally triumph over the past, as it did with Lenny. Every one was different, though not as different as Dawn.

In 1997, with my best means of support closed down, I needed to leave the Isle of Wight to seek work. Sad really, the Island is regularly short of psychiatrists willing to live and work on the Island – but a man with my credentials was unwelcome. So on my departure, Dawn decided she needed support, so she advertised for those interested in setting up a 'panic attack support group', whereupon her living room was filled with people with panic attacks. On doing a 'go round' in which each has their say in turn, Dawn recognised why they were having their panic attacks, and asked if she could tell them. When they agreed, she did so, they discussed it for a number of weeks, got better and closed the group.

I must have treated 100s of patients – Dawn was the first to take up the challenge, and then repeat the process with others I never met. Here we have sessions 6 and 7 for one such, whom I here call Louise. These sessions took place some time in 2004 – the time is meticulously marked, but the date is not. What appears here is what was typed in via a closed chat room on the internet. Remarkable how these things work.

Here we have session 6, so the work to be done has already been well discussed. Louise has clearly just sent a letter to her parents, which she hopes will clarify the relationship between them – later in these sessions, we find this has only limited usefulness – it is not the parents who need to change, or be brought up to date.

Dawn uses the word "link" as one of her 'spanners', to encourage the sufferer to trace back the terrors which afflict her today, to their true origin in the distant past. And here we see it working over coffee – the rational mind coming to see the roots of the emotion, and beginning to control them, rather than the other way around.

Dawn begins to explore the question as to whether the infantile relationship with parents is still extant. Clearly if a parent rejects an infant, that infant dies. However if a parent looses go of an adult, that adult can flourish. Louise gives a delicious account of the battle in her mind between the old style – reject your parents and you're dead, which in infancy is true – and today's reality where co-existence on an equal emotional level is now truer.

The notion of 'waterproof' is again short hand for becoming impervious to noxious parental influences. The difference between the parental figment in the mind, and today's actual parent needs to be clarified. Today you are on an equal footing with your parent – then they held your life or death in their not always competent hands. As with Lenny before, there is no need for animosity – just clarity.

SESSION 6

Louise: (10:30:08): Hi Dawn, like the photo!

: (10:30:46): You there?

Dawn: (10:31:24): Oops sorry. Just reading notes

: (10:31:36): So how has your week been?

Lu: (10:32:27): Well, still feeling very anxious. Very teary and finding simple things very difficult.

Dn: (10:32:43): Awww. So did you send the letter?

Lu: (10:33:02): Yes. They must have got it today.

Dn: (10:33:24): hhmm. So I guess you are worrying about that?

Lu: (10:33:40): Yes. I'm sure that has a lot to do with it.

Dn: (10:34:01): So what has been happening this week and did you manage to link?

Lu: (10:36:34): I took Freda to a music session and felt really anxious when I was in there with her. Closed door, no means of escape etc. I realise it is directly to do with negative self-talk. Tried to remind myself why I was feeling like that and told myself I was 34, not 4 etc. The feeling did go off and I managed to stay in the situation and then have coffee with the mums afterwards.

Dn: (10:37:04): Well that's great!!!

Lu: (10:37:10): Do you have any other ways of linking? Is there more to it than I understand?

Dn: (10:38:14): Well yes, but you learn it in stages really, I think you have to look at the need that you have.

: (10:38:36): Do you know that you need them?

Lu: (10:38:51): My parents?

Dn: (10:39:14): Yes

: (10:39:29): Do you think you need them?

Lu: (10:42:47): I have difficulty with the absolutism of this theory. On a conscious level I realise and feel that I definitely don't need them to survive. But there doesn't seem to be room for a middle ground, whereby you are allowed to want them in your life. Do you know what I mean? You said you and your parents are polite to one another and remember birthdays etc. I find that amazing that you still want them in your life, even in that small extent, given the things they have done to you. I'm confused about what is normal to feel. Does that make sense?

Dn: (10:44:02): Yes it does. It's just a matter of being water proof against them, do you follow?

: (10:44:51): Once you no longer fear the rejection of your parents then you are water proof and free to be you.

Here Dawn emphasises that fear of rejection is the bane of adult life. The reality is – it was before. Now, if your parents reject you, it's the same as any other adult rejecting you – it's their loss.

Why should Louise be fearful? The only possible reason is that infantile emotional reactions tell her to be frightened their rejection will kill her. This is the obsolete terror – often deeply embedded, and often difficult to shift. But being obsolete, it has only one way to go – and once it's gone, you're rid of it forever.

Again, there is no difficulty in needing your parents for everyday support today – we all need support. It's only needing them for life-support that creates enormous difficulties – this was true, it was the only truth, but is neither any longer. Mutual support is what we sociable animals do best – dependent support is what neonates are born with, and with support and education, can grow out of.

Guilt, which Louise mentions, is described in *Emotional Health* as just one more disguise for fear. Here the link with fear of parental rejection is brought very much to the fore

And "being alone" could well be cover for being parentless – a state which all infants abominate, and all adults should be able to take with a pinch of salt. The human mind can create some wonderful patterns – especially when it is trying to disguise what is really going on. All emotional support does is provide a secure context for bringing this underlying (and now decidedly obsolete) reality into the full light of the present day.

Words such as "safety net", or "tight rope" give the game away – we are not talking everyday maternal concerns, or at least not only those – we are talking life and death issues, suitably confused so as not to be directly confronted.

Gentle persuasion is the order of the day – Louise, like all sufferers would prefer to be well, if only they could see a safe way to get there. This is the basis of emotional support – the assumption that they can, and given support, will assuredly achieve that.

Dn: (10:45:42): You wont put up with their behaviour, and that will then depend on the type of relationship that you will have.

Lu: (10:46:45): I certainly feel I have had enough of their behaviour, but I must still be fearful of their response. How do I get to the point where I am water proof?

Dn: (10:47:57): OK. Well you are water proof when you don't need them!!!!!

: (10:48:19): Can you tell them that they were lousy parents to their face?

: (10:48:35): Without fear?

Lu: (10:50:03): This telling them to their face business is difficult because we don't live nearby. I think the letter is the first step to this. But it would be a bolt out of the blue unless I prepared the ground. I am still fearful.

Dn: (10:51:34): You see doing it to their face is what is important. For you are facing your fear, or not as the case maybe!!! And by doing this, you will know that you are in control of your life today, not them.

: (10:52:05): And if you are rejected by them you won't DIE!!!

: (10:52:21): You can do this by role-play.

: (10:52:44): Can you imagine them in front of you, and tell them they were lousy parents?

: (10:53:06): Tell me how it makes you feel?

Lu: (10:53:48): Yes, I have done this with Roger before. It makes me feel guilty - for Mum - and fearful - towards Dad.

Dn: (10:54:11): Well under guilt there is always fear.

: (10:54:23): So tell me what are you fearful of?

Lu: (10:54:34): Being alone.

Dn: (10:54:51): OK so what will happen if you are alone?

Lu: (10:55:20): Well, nothing really.

Dn: (10:55:33): OK so why the fear?

: (10:55:54): You must be fearing something?

Lu: (10:57:15): It keeps coming back to this feeling of wanting what everybody else around me has - extended family. I feel lonely and I suppose the fear is, "who will take care of the kids if I or Roger can't". I don't feel I have a safety net under me and life is a tightrope.

Dn: (10:58:26): Well you see that's the thing. Being alone was how you felt as a child, right?

Lu: (10:58:52): Yes.

What Dawn does here is bring in facts from today's reality. And Louise's reaction is gratifying. From a vague, wouldn't an "extended family" be nice, to "God no," when the offer is made for this to become a practical reality.

As you read through the remainder of session 6, bear in mind how Dawn repeatedly guides Louise back to the painful topic – the issue of whether parents are still life-saving, or whether they should no longer be. The key is the persistence of infantile survival strategies – the technique is persuasion, gradually pointing out that the dogmas from before, are unsustainable today – provided the link, the connection, the logical sequence is followed through. The Truth will set you free, in this case free from the shackles of inept parenting.

Dn: (10:59:16): So would you want mum and dad to look after your kids if say anything did happen to you?
Lu: (10:59:32): No! God no!
Dn: (11:00:06): Well then do you see what you are wanting is totally unhealthy. Why inflict that on the kids!!!!!!!!!!!!
  : (11:00:31): This is your need kicking in – do you see?
  : (11:01:08): And as for life being a tightrope, you are saying you may DIE
Lu: (11:01:26): Yes, I see that. It is the idea of supportive parents/grandparents, not the reality of the people involved.
Dn: (11:01:46): RIGHT
  : (11:02:01): Your parents are not supportive. Why would you want that?
  : (11:02:15): You see it's the frozen childhood fear saying that
  : (11:02:39): The 34 year old says NO THANK YOU
  : (11:02:53): Do you see?
Lu: (11:03:54): Yes. It is my age old problem of measuring myself up against other people and wanting what they have got.
  : (11:04:06): Which is childish.
Dn: (11:04:34): Yes and once the fear of mum and dad has gone you will realign yourself.
  : (11:05:10): That is why you have to look at the 34 yr old and weigh up if it is adult or not
  : (11:05:28): And if its not, then it's the need creeping in.
  : (11:05:43): So tell me what do you need them for?
Lu: (11:06:15): Nothing. In fact they cause me more pain than comfort.
Dn: (11:06:36): Right. So can you tell them this?

Lu: (11:07:04): I did, in the letter. Do you think I need to go and actually tell them face to face?

Dn: (11:07:22): Well role play it. Can you do it now?

Lu: (11:07:30): Yes.

Dn: (11:07:42): tell me how you feel when you say it out loud?

Lu: (11:09:00): Well, it's very emotional. I imagined Mum and Dad's images being blown away.

Dn: (11:09:14): OK. So what do they say?

Lu: (11:09:40): They don't want it. They are objecting.

Dn: (11:09:59): OK. And how do you feel?

Lu: (11:10:25): A bit better.

Dn: (11:10:39): OK are you angry about their behaviour?

Lu: (11:12:12): Yes. I'm realising how they have perpetuated this dependency. Mum doesn't have a life of her own so tries to live through me and my sister.

Dn: (11:12:39): So can you tell them both now that you are angry at them?

Lu: (11:13:13): Yes. It's a powerful thing to say to someone isn't it?

Dn: (11:13:30): Oh yes it is. So you can role play this, can you?

Lu: (11:13:54): Yes.

Dn: (11:14:06): And how does it feel to tell them that

Lu: (11:15:08): I've role played it before. I think I have a fear of letting my feelings out and crying in front of them. Of losing control.

Dn: (11:15:26): Why? Do you think they will belittle you ?

Lu: (11:16:29): Yes. That I will appear weak and vulnerable. And that my Mum will seize on this as a way of taking control again. "Let me make you a nice cup of tea and we'll forget all about this silly nonsense". That sort of thing.

Dn: (11:17:00): Ha ha!!! and what do you say to that???

Lu: (11:17:36): No. This is real. Face up to it.

Dn: (11:17:57): And if she wont, then what will you say?

Lu: (11:19:10): That is her choice. I am facing up to it and I'm no longer happy to pretend.

Dn: (11:19:39): So what about GET LOST mum and dad?

Lu: (11:20:54): Hmmm. That seems too abusive. I have to be able to live with what I have said and done. That is why I fear talking face to face. I fear I will lose my temper and say things I don't mean.

Dn: (11:21:24): What? You don't mean them to leave you alone?

Lu: (11:21:25): Or maybe things I do mean but am too scared to say unless in anger.

Dn: (11:21:45): Don't you want them to leave you alone then?

Lu: (11:22:21): Yes. I do want then to leave me alone. But I'd have to say, I don't want a relationship with you as it stands.

Dn: (11:23:23): OK well try and tell them that you don't want a relationship with them any more, can you say that?
Lu: (11:23:58): Yes. Doing that.
Dn: (11:24:15): OK when you have said it out loud, tell me what you felt.
Lu: (11:24:47): More in control.
Dn: (11:24:56): GREAT!!!!!!!!!!!!
   : (11:25:29): Do you see that you need to be in charge and you are allowed to be.
   : (11:25:46): and how much better you feel when you do have that.
Lu: (11:26:53): Yes. It's also being able to keep the courage of your convictions. I felt good after writing the letter, but lost heart a bit in between writing it and plucking up the courage again to send it.
Dn: (11:27:43): this is where you have to battle your childhood defences and remain the adult.
   : (11:28:00): So what do you think you have learnt today?
Lu: (11:28:17): Yes. Recognising the thoughts for what they are. That's the tricky bit. They don't come colour coded do they?!
Dn: (11:28:36): No they don't, so you have to do lots of role play
   : (11:28:42): Lots
   : (11:29:00): How do you think it has gone today?
Lu: (11:29:54): Good. I appreciate you running over time a bit. I have felt a bit frustrated in the past by running out of time. I wonder if you would consider doing a longer session?
Dn: (11:30:35): Sure this is possible. Would you like longer on the next one. An hour and a half be OK?
Lu: (11:31:09): Yes please. Can you do 10.30 am on Friday?
Dn: (11:31:14): Let me look
Lu: (11:31:29): I should have a headset by then as well.
Dn: (11:32:07): I am out all morning Friday but evening is OK. How is that for you?
Lu: (11:32:26): Yes. OK. 7 pm?
Dn: (11:32:46): Sure that's fine.
   : (11:33:04): We have group on Thursday at 7 pm
Lu: (11:33:09): Great. And I'll log in to the group.
Dn: (11:33:27): OK. Great Louise. Keep role playing OK?
Lu: (11:33:45): Yes, OK. Will do. Thanks Dawn. Bye.
Dn: (11:34:06): Take care chat soon

Session 7 opens with Louise discussing the reply she received to the letter she sent to her parents, as mentioned in session 6. Dawn gradually helps her untangle her mixed responses. It really makes gripping reading, to see how she gradually grows in confidence, just as

Lenny did. The words used, the spanners, vary, as they must since each grew up differently. But the release that the sufferer feels as they put their own template onto their powerful fears – this is the same throughout. And the template too is always the same – grow away from childhood survival strategies. But do this only with consent, by persuasion – there is no other way, if you want to change mental furniture, either your own or anyone else's.

SESSION 7

Dn: (19:04:54): Hi Louise.
Lu: (19:06:54): Hi Dawn. I have a headset, but I don't know if it is working! I have just been going through the set-up process for BT Communicator.
Dn: (19:08:00): Ohhh OK. Well let's hope we can get that working for next time then. So how have you been doing?
Lu: (19:10:43): Well, I got a short reply from Mum today. She says she doesn't have such bad memories of the past and that she is shattered by it all. She also says my Dad is going to write to me and begins the letter by saying we have always loved you and will always continue to do so. But there is no apology, no acknowledgement that what I'm saying is true and no attempt to look at any of it.
Dn: (19:11:19): So how did you feel?
Lu: (19:14:48): Well, it's been an odd day really. Freda is ill and so I spent all morning snuggled in bed with her, which left me feeling a bit like I'd wasted the day - guilty. Even though I couldn't have done anything other than look after the poor soul. Coming down to the letter made me feel worse and I ended up having a few tears. But I'm starting to feel better now. The letter from Dad is like a threat, though. I'm sure it will be hellfire and brimstone. "How can you do this to your poor mother, she has done nothing but given you the best years of her life" and so on. Heard it before.
Dn: (19:16:27): Well at least you are aware that this is the tactics they play. The point is will you fall for it?
Lu: (19:17:37): No. I'm absolutely certain this is the right thing to do. I only had to observe the effect getting that letter had on me to realise the truth, in the fact that the anxiety is coming from my relationship with them.
Dn: (19:18:11): Good. I am glad you can see that. So tell me why you have anxiety and how it works.
Lu: (19:18:56): Hmmm. Not sure I understand the question. Why one has anxiety in general? Or me specifically?
Dn: (19:19:31): Well could you explain to someone why you have anxiety?

: (19:19:58): Where it comes from etc

Lu: (19:25:07): Right. Yes. I think it is an exaggerated response to general worries and concerns. We all experience some form of anxiety but with me it gets cranked right up. It comes from the emotion fear. And from experiencing that emotion as a child, being so frightened by an event that I simply put the whole thing in a box and refused to look at it. As a young adult I didn't have the emotional maturity to deal with difficulties and began to panic, attaching fear to everyday experiences like going to the cinema etc. More specifically, my landmine seems to be facing up to my parents and letting them know I don't rate their parenting and that I won't let me treat me badly anymore. Although I'm aware that I might have another one!

Dn: (19:26:32): OK. So what is the solution for this?

Lu: (19:27:32): To divorce them, metaphorically at least, although I seem to be doing it literally as well. To become "water-proof " to them.

Dn: (19:27:52): So what do you have to say to them?

Lu: (19:28:10): I don't need you.

: (19:28:40): And I don't want you. Not on these terms.

Dn: (19:28:53): Why don't you need them?

Lu: (19:29:18): Because I'm not a child and I won't die without them.

Dn: (19:29:30): GREAT!!!!!!

: (19:29:37): But do you believe it?

Lu: (19:29:55): Yes, I do. I feel better just typing it.

Dn: (19:30:21): That's good, so you shouldn't have another panic attack then right?

Lu: (19:30:47): Do you really think so? I wish I could be so sure.

Dn: (19:31:17): Well if you believe what you say then of course you wont because there will be nothing left to fear

Lu: (19:31:46): My feeling is, I will find my Dad's letter difficult.

Dn: (19:32:03): Hhmmm and why would that be?

Lu: (19:34:09): Just that it will hurt me. I'll be all right and will bounce back, but I have never been able to hear/read things that are unpleasant to me without it having an impact. I feel it is something I have just got to get over and done with.

Dn: (19:35:12): But you have to be waterproof so this will not effect you and you will just laugh at his behaviour

Lu: (19:37:36): Yes. I'm hoping he will show himself up for what he is. If he starts ranting and raving then I will laugh at him. If he does the old "we're devastated" routine I'll find it harder. I get the feeling Mum has had a big hysterical tantrum. Her letter is only five or six lines. Hardly seems worth sending it and it isn't very coherent.

Dn: (19:39:10): So if he was to say that you were a naughty girl for speaking up and saying how you feel, what will you say?

Lu: (19:39:33): Get lost!

Dn: (19:39:54): Well that is clear!!!

  : (19:40:03): Does it feel good to say that

Lu: (19:41:15): That's what I would feel like saying. I'd probably temper it by saying it was high time I spoke up and stood-up for myself. Yes, it does feel good. He is a bully, pure and simple. And Mum is manipulative.

Dn: (19:41:52): Sounds like you have them logged

Lu: (19:42:07): I feel guilty because sometimes I wish he would just die. I know things would be better with Mum then.

Dn: (19:42:49): Why feel guilty?

Lu: (19:45:19): Well, I feel it is a bad thing to wish on someone. He is 20 years older than my Mum, so we have always known she would be left on her own. I think the age thing has coloured our entire lives. Mum feels she has to look after him now. And he has always dictated to her over decisions, money matters etc. He is like a father figure to her. She will no doubt want to be more involved with us when he goes. Trouble is, I don't want to know now.

Dn: (19:46:04): But you say she is manipulating too

  : (19:46:47): I think your mum has her own frozen emotions!!!

Lu: (19:47:07): Yes. She lacks confidence and has hidden away from the world so lacks experience too. Her way of getting what she wants is to manipulate other people to do it for her. I try to be assertive and she hates it.

Dn: (19:47:27): Yes, she would do

Lu: (19:50:53): She certainly does! She consistently refuses to examine anything faintly difficult. Hence Dad is the one writing the real letter. She has actually said in past emails "I can't go over this again". She is extremely immature. She even has a baby voice and baby words she uses to my Dad. Or used to anyway. It used to make me want to scream. Basically I have been protecting her from the truth all these years. She couldn't even stand it when me and my sisters would get together other than when we visited the family home. Controlling and afraid.

Dn: (19:51:51): I know it is so sad, but you have to let her be responsible for her own actions

Lu: (19:52:55): And yet I just feel sorry for her. I oscillate between loathing her and feeling sorry for her. I've tried to force her to deal with life more maturely but all she would say is "I'm a package. You can't change people".

Dn: (19:54:00): This is very sad. But if she can see her family taking charge of their lives, then this may just inspire her to do something.

Lu: (19:54:37): I really hope so. That's a good way of looking at it. Lead by example. It makes me feel better about it.

Dn: (19:55:37): Well you can only hope that by you doing something it will help her too,. If it doesn't, this is not your fault.

Lu: (19:56:07): Yes. I don't feel responsible for her happiness anymore.

Dn: (19:56:54): That's good. As you are an individual and responsible for your actions not hers or your dads.

Lu: (19:59:22): Yes. Saying they will have tantrums was a good way of making me realise there is nothing I can or should do about the way they respond to things. That is entirely up to them. Other parents on getting a letter such as that, would behave very differently I am sure. So do you think there is any chance things will ever improve? It feels very weird thinking about sending them Christmas presents. How do you feel about honouring those traditions still with your parents?

Dn: (20:01:10): I really can't say what your parents will do, but as for mine, well it is like giving cards and small gifts to say my daughter's teacher. There is no emotion involved now.

    : (20:01:28): This may seem cold but that is all that is left really.

    : (20:01:52): We are polite to one another and that is it really.

Lu: (20:03:19): Do you know of anybody that has been in this situation that has managed to create a healthy relationship with their parents? I don't know if my friends are waterproof to their parents, you know. They must still be dependent on them, otherwise they wouldn't accept their help, don't you think?

Dn: (20:04:43): I think it is fine to accept help from parents if it is needed. That is quite healthy, but parents should aim to bring their children up to be independent of them.

Lu: (20:06:20): It must be a fine line though. If your mother looks after your child two days a week while you work that isn't being independent is it? If your parents have paid for your house extension, that isn't being independent either. These are real examples, by the way.

Dn: (20:08:11): I think that to look after a child is fine. That is just the same as a baby sitter. It's when you won't use anyone BUT mum to babysit. And paying for things doesn't show independence but a loan I think is fine.

Lu: (20:09:16): I read in the paper that something like half a million UK parents still give their "children" over 30 years old "pocket money". Amazing eh?

Dn: (20:09:44): Yes it is very sad. So do you think you still need them?

Lu: (20:11:04): Nah. I don't. And I don't want them to look after my children etc. Everything I have achieved I have done so on my own. My friends can't say that.

Dn: (20:11:44): Well that's really good. I am pleased for you. So do you think you need any more sessions?

Lu: (20:12:35): I would like to, yes. I need to test out the no more panic attacks theory. Is this how it went for you?

Dn: (20:14:28): Pretty much so. But yes, test it out, it may seem a bit scary to start with being free in reality. But as you are seeing, it is so much better than the fear you have been living in.

Lu: (20:16:17): Did you just no longer feel fearful in situations you had always experienced panic in? Won't I have to push through the fear to get there? With me, it is not so much the having a panic attack that is the problem, it is the feeling of unreality and being on the verge of a panic for a long time that gets me.

   : (20:17:06): A general heightened state of anxiety that could, at any minute, kick off into a full-blown attack.

Dn: (20:17:28): This is the point. There will be no unreal feeling as you wont be fearful anymore as you don't need them.

   : (20:18:40): Your confidence will just keep rising and as long as you keep linking,

Lu: (20:19:11): Sounds great! But when I am anxious I am not thinking "I need my Mummy" I'm thinking "Oh God, I'm in a cinema and wouldn't it be terrible if I had a panic attack now."

Dn: (20:20:08): Well as I said if you link before you get anxious then you can break the out of date defences.

Lu: (20:20:55): Right. So can you give me some good sayings to draw on? I've got the "I am 34 not 4" one, which is helpful.

Dn: (20:21:37): OK well what about I don't need mum anymore.

   : (20:21:42): or dad

   : (20:22:07): If you link and add this on the end you will find it shall help.

Lu: (20:22:47): Do you know anyone that has had a problem with driving and how have they managed their recovery with it?

   : (20:22:57): Driving

Dn: (20:23:27): Yes many, they get to a point and feel that they cant go any further

   : (20:23:41): and start to feel panicky

   : (20:25:07): But they have linked it through that they are....yrs old and they are not a child, its just telling yourself the reality and that your parents are wrong and shouting GET LOST like you did to them at the end of a sentence is good too.

Lu: (20:26:53): OK. It is a fine line for me with driving because there is obviously a real danger there. It is knowing how far to push myself.

Dn: (20:27:33): Well go slowly to start with. Don't push it. Just go at your own speed, there is no race.

   : (20:28:01): So would you like to arrange another 1-1 or do you want to just let me know?

Lu: (20:29:17): I would like to arrange another one if that is OK with you. But let's just go to one a week for now. Is Wednesday at 9.15 am any good to you?

Dn: (20:29:39): Let me check

   : (20:30:42): sorry I have a 1-1 at that time 11 am is fine

Lu: (20:31:36): Also, while I think of it, do you or Bob have anything to say about the role of hormone balance in relation to increased anxiety and panic? I have a friend who experiences acute anxiety symptoms only when she is pregnant or breast feeding. I went on the pill recently because I found my cycle was making everything worse. I have a couple of other examples as well. 11 am is fine.

Dn: (20:33:17): Well yes I think your anxiety does sway your hormone balance – it did with me. and fear also depletes the chemical levels in the brain hence depression.

   : (20:33:53): As for your friend, while feeding and being pregnant I think it because it is putting her in an adult role.

Lu: (20:35:01): So you don't think it is the other way round then? That the hormone imbalance creates or exacerbates anxiety?

Dn: (20:36:08): No I don't think so. They say that in the menopause your anxiety goes up, so I guess it is debatable.

Lu: (20:38:00): Food for thought. Would you ask Bob his view on this? I could be wrong, but my perception is that more women than men experience anxiety problems. What would happen if we were given testosterone? Apart from growing beards of course?!

 Dn: (20:39:21): Well OK I shall email him and see what he says on the matter and let you know, I have to go now so I shall see you on Wednesday at 11 am,

Lu: (20:39:46): Thanks Dawn. Just quickly, how is your daughter?

Dn: (20:40:15): by the way you are doing BRILLIANTLY!!!!!!!!!!

There are several points to make. First, the utter clarity with which these tangled issues must be faced. Then the 100% conviction that all these symptoms arise from obsolete reactions, out of date emotions. Thirdly the complete trust on the part of the sufferer that by allowing examination of these painful, indeed terrifying items, there will be a resolution, a healing of them all. It is clear from the above that these issues are repeatedly voiced, and as calmly dealt with.

What follows next is a session I had, which shows just how complicated these matters can become, and how critical it is to keep a flexible creative approach, while maintaining 100% conviction that any, indeed all irrational emotions arise from something that has lain unresolved since childhood.

7) EMOTION SUPPORT for Ann

This is the last of three chapters presenting dialogues to show how emotions can confuse. They are intended to illustrate how denial can utilise any quantity of mental resources to further its aim, which is to deny access to today's daylight those items which have become too frightening. In this instance I am the one attempting to unravel a dilemma that has completely fooled an otherwise well balanced, confident individual.

As you read through, bear in mind that this is how the human mind cripples itself. The resolution, when it comes, was a surprise to me, and indeed to Ann, who had spent many long hours wrestling with it, in the hope that she could solve it without the need to come to see me with it. But this resolution is only available to us at this time, because we know each other well, we trust each other, and both of us are well familiar with how terror induces denial. These are the positive ingredients – without them progress would have been impossible.

It goes to show that for severe mental distress, as in the psychoses, identical deep seated problems are wrecking mental lives. And the prospect of resolution is repeatedly denied – since the precursor ingredients of confidence in the resolution and abundant trust are too thin on the ground. However, where the latter flourish, then no mental disease of any severity is intractable – all succumb to Emotion Support and Emotion Education.

The situation is desperate. Ann is about to undergo an operation the following day, involving a general anaesthetic. She is convinced that her panic attacks will drive her to distraction, just as the needle is about to be placed. She had a panic attack during her last major operation, but it started just after the needle had gone in, so they were able to push her back, as she relapsed into unconsciousness. On this occasion she has had a long time to anticipate it, and she now seriously contemplates leaping off the operating table and running. Shades of Lenny beating a retreat, except that here she is desperate for the operation to go through, and be a success.

Now I had treated Ann for severe panic attacks over a prolonged period, some time ago. She had done remarkably well. She was about to re-marry, had acquired an interesting new job, and things were at last going smoothly for her. And yet, despite all this, up jump the old horrors to decimate her recent successes.

For my part, I was totally non-plussed. Indeed the first section shows me trying one avenue, and then another, while success continues to elude us both. We had already in our earlier lengthy sessions given the remnants of her earlier dysfunctional attachment to her parents a thorough airing. The general absence of panic attacks since we last had a session served to indicate that all was quiet in that regard.

My comments in this third dialogue are briefer. Those who have worked their way through the earlier two, will have an idea of what to look out for. Though it is scarcely edifying to see me floundering, and initially failing dismally to find a pathway through – at least this does emphasise the constant trying, the robust determination on both our parts that there is a way through, and that whatever may currently appear to be the case, if there are irrationalities, then they must, perforce, arise elsewhere. If it takes a while, and a quantity of peregrinations, then so be it – persevere is our joint motto – and here is the result.

TRANSCRIPTION OF AUDIO TAPE

[Pauses marked as '. . .']

Bob: So, how are you and what is going wrong?
Ann: Ah (Laughing) Don't know. Can't make any sense of this one. Oh, bloody thing. I can't seem to work through this fear that I am going to die when I go under the anaesthetic. Um, I

can't. Logically, I know, and all the rest of it but there is a mental block there.

Bob: Coming from somewhere else?

Ann: Yes. And the bastard, bloody thing – I can't work it out.

Bob: OK. So we need to go back, don't we?

Ann: We do, but where are we going?

Bob: So, still in control, losing control, or somebody else being in control, like your Dad. Is he in control?

Ann: No.

Bob: What would you do if he was?

Ann: If he was in control?

Bob: Yes. He says, "Yes, all right, I am taking over, you can't do anything you want". What are you going to say?

Ann: I would laugh at him!

Bob: Would you?

Ann: Yes! Stupid bloke! Oh dear, if my mum did it, I'd just feel sad for her and say "Shut up you stupid woman, you can't!" I know, I'd just laugh at them. There isn't that control there. They can't control me any more.

Bob: So who can?

Ann: Only me.

So we've drawn a blank on Dad. Even when bounced around a little, it seems unlikely we will make any progress pursuing Dad. Mum too seems pretty much a dead issue. But somehow, the key lies in a past trauma – we need to persevere until we find it. Having waved the issue of loss of control, and found no takers, I next try confined spaces.

Bob: Right. So something happened.

Ann: Yeah, I know.

Bob: Were you in a cupboard or locked up or in a confined space?

Ann: Um, I remember being put in a wardrobe once by my brother. My brother used to do a lot of . . .

Bob: How old is your brother compared to you?

Ann: Two years older.

Bob: He put you in wardrobe, right. Tell me about that.

Ann: Well I can't remember much about it. I just remember being in there and not being able to get out and my leg being out of joint. So obviously I didn't like the confined space. But I don't remember much about it. But I remember banging to get out and someone opening the door and me falling out. And I remember the pain in my hip. But I don't particularly remember fear. It was more pain because of the hip but I don't remember it being frightening.

Bob: Were you angry with him?

Ann: No, no. I don't think it was him, or I might have just climbed in there myself. I don't know, it was the only time I can remember being confined in.

Bob: How old were you?

Ann: I don't know, maybe seven, about age seven.

Bob: But you should remember.

Ann: I remember being in there.

Bob: Who put you in there?

Ann: I don't know, I really don't remember who put me in there. I don't remember. I mean a lot of the things my brother did do to me I do remember.

Bob: Such as?

Ann: Oh, he used to try and shoot me with an air rifle. What else did he do? He had a favourite trick which I used to be very, very frightened of and he would get the blankets and pin them down on top of me so I couldn't move and I couldn't get out. He used to take great delight in that one. And that was very frightening, I do remember that.

Bob: That's what they're going to do again, isn't it?

Ann: What?

Bob: Pin you down.

Ann: But they not are they?

Bob: You don't believe that all together?

Ann: No, I know they aren't going to pin me down.

Bob: Let's put your brother in the frame, what are you going to say to him?

Ann: I can't what?

Bob: Anything.

Ann: I don't know. At one point I remember being angry at him.

Bob: About time isn't it?

Ann: Well I was angry at him for, not for the things he did actually. I was angry at him for rejecting me. Because when it came all out in the open, he decided that he was going to side with mum and dad on this one. Even though we had a private conversation and he admitted some of the abuse had taken part for him. He decided he couldn't own up to that. And so, to close it for him, he would shove me out of the way, and I was really angry.

Bob: What age were you then?

Ann: When this all came out when we were in our twenties.

Bob: And then you got angry for him rejecting you then?

Ann: Yeah, because he pushed me and isolated me, and not stood with me on this, even though he admitted that he had taken some abuse from them too.

Bob: I see. He admitted taking the abuse but didn't say so to them.

Ann: No, he wouldn't. He never could.

Bob: So where is he now?

Ann: He lives in Y.

Bob: Do you see much of him?

Ann: No he won't speak to me no more.

Bob: Because?

Ann: Because of all this.

Bob: From the age of about 20?

Ann: Yeah.

Bob: Crazy isn't it?

Ann: Yes, I was very, very angry at him for doing that. But then I had to look at it and understand why he was doing it. Because he was terrified himself, and me, I just opened the can of worms and it was too much for him. And I guess his defences are – push me out of the way so I don't exist, so I can't bring it up.

Bob: What were you saying yesterday?

Ann: I don't know, I would love to have that relationship back with him.

Bob: Why?

Ann: Because he is my brother and I love him. It wasn't our fault that happened to us.

Bob: Well he's not going to say that is he?

Ann: No, the funny thing was. . . Oh shit! There is a big wasp there behind you. . . . I forget what I was going to say.

Bob: "The funny thing was. . ." about your brother.

Ann: Yes, he did say when we had the very first discussion and I told him why I was having panic attacks and everything and sort of explained everything to him and that's when he opened up and said well actually I took some of the abuse too.

Bob: When was this '95? '97?

Ann: Yes, when I was coming to see you.

Bob: Ten years?

Ann: Yes. He actually said to me then – he said look, he went away that night and he was sort of. . . he was just wanting to confront Dad because his daughter was down with my parents. And he wanted to know why I wouldn't leave my children down there. And so I had to tell the whole story to him. And he was unsure as to whether he was going to go get his daughter, or whether he was going to leave her there. Well he obviously chose to leave her there and ignore me.

But he walked out and said to me, "Look if you ever need anything you want to talk through – if you want me or anything, just call me." And I was really pleased, I thought that was really cool – he's understood, he's opened up to me, I'd opened up to him and we could work through this together. Then he just shut me off and he wouldn't answer the phone anymore, he wouldn't speak to me. And I was very, very angry about that. But as I say, I understood why he was doing it. So I can understand that.

Bob: So why didn't you get angry with him tying you down with blankets?

Ann: Um.

Bob: You should have been, shouldn't you?

Ann: I don't know whether I should have been as a child or not. I don't know.

Bob: If he did it to you now, what would you do?

Ann: I'd tell him to piss off!

Bob: You'd get angry wouldn't you?

Ann: Yeah, too right I would.

Bob: There's nothing wrong with that is there? So why didn't you get angry earlier on?

Ann: Because, I guess the fear took over.

Bob: That's right.

Ann: The fear was there and it was too great to do anything, and reinforced by mum as well.

Bob: Saying?

Ann: Well, a number of things. But it would never be in favour of me It would be that we were playing about.

Bob: Let's examine, he's pinning you down with the blankets when you're small and you should be angry with him. So why aren't you?

Ann: I don't know. As I said the fear. . . What now? Why am I angry about that now?

Bob: Well both. Let's go back then first.

Ann: I don't know why I wasn't angry then. I think it was just too great a fear and I wasn't backed up by mum.

Bob: Well it was your mum's position that it was your fault anyway.

Ann: Possibly, or it was our fault we were messing about and then she'd come along and bash our heads together and tell us to shut up, really.

Bob: Just the two of you was there?

Ann: Yes, I had an older sister but she'd left home by then.

Bob: How old is she?

Ann: Um, she's 14-16 years older than me. She was from my mum's first marriage.

Bob: OK. So you are what now, how old are you now?

Ann: 39 now.

Bob: So he is 41 and she is 50 something?
I think it's the blanket.

Ann: I don't know.

I'm not doing too well here. I'm just scratching around in the dark, trying to hook something with my baited line. So far, there's very little to show for it. All I've got going is the blanket, not terribly promising. But, though I didn't comment on it directly, I must have clocked that she "loved" her brother – which did not add up 100% with her strong reaction to his recent rejection – but then again, perhaps it did . . .

Bob: What symptoms do you get? Describe your feelings? What happens?

Ann: What? When I think about what?

Bob: About the general anaesthetic?

Ann: Well, I think it through. I mean I have been battling the last couple of days, I have been pushing myself to the limit, to really think about it. And I get to a point where they put the needle in my hand and it just goes into a blind panic, it goes woof. . . The anxiety will just overtake and it is sheer panic. It's terror and fear, and I know it is.

Bob: Good. And it's terror and fear of what?

Ann: I don't know. I guess that I am going to cease to exist, I don't know. I would imagine that I am going to die! It has to be! But I don't know. Like I said to Tom when they put me off, when I went up there last week for the tests, and they decided that I wasn't enough weeks, and that pissed me off.

Bob: Good, because it should do.

Ann: You know. They couldn't give me a reasonable explanation. Um, but they said they'd prefer me to wait until this week. As I walked out, I was absolutely, I was relieved! I said to Tom I felt that I had been on death row all week.

Bob: Wow!

Ann: I really did feel. . . And I was preparing things. I could see it, that I was preparing that after Friday, I was going to cease to exist. So I had to fit things in, plan things out for my family and I could see myself doing it. And I thought, fucking hell! I couldn't get to grips with why, and I'm still not now, but I'm trying to bring it in perspective. I am trying to put reality in there all the time. And I've done a good job because I stopped preparing. I'm getting there, but I still think up until, you know, I think it through and the injection goes in – and that's when the panic goes again.

So I am thinking what the hell is going to happen when I actually do do it. What am I going to do? Am I going to freak? Or will I be so subdued about it and so resigning in the fact I'm going to die, or. . . How am I going to take this? And I don't know how I am going to react, and that's scary! Not knowing what I am going to do. Because I don't feel in control. If that helps any.

Now this is serious. Here we have a mature adult, a sensible enough person. She recently bought and sold a house, she got engaged, her marriage is coming up in a week or two – all carefully, and sensibly sorted – yet here she is, actively, carefully and consciously preparing for her own annihilation by a medical team who only wish to assist her with her current medical problem. How irrational can you get?

Bob: You don't feel in control of what? Of them or you?

Ann: Of the situation, of knowing what's going to happen.

Bob: Fear of you freaking out?

Ann: Well I don't know. . .

Bob: Well let's have you freaking out. What are you going to do? Well you go "Ok, I'm freaking out!" Give me a demo of what you're going to do?

Ann: Well, as I said to Tom, they will have to dart me because I will be running. And I know. . .

Bob: You will jump off the table! And run off!

Ann: Yes, there are two choices. I am going to run or I am going. . . Other wise I'm going to be so subdued and I am going to be complacent, and go "OK, that's it, that's my lot, I am gone." I don't know. I don't know which way I am going to go. And that is not nice knowing.

Bob: OK, so it is either run or what shall we say resign? Right?

Ann: Yeah.

Bob: So what we do is take that back to this blanket thing.

Ann: Right, well I couldn't run, because my brother was on top of me with the blanket. So I couldn't run and I definitely wasn't resigned, because I was panicking and was struggling to get out. So I didn't lay there and resign to it.

Bob: You were obviously terrified.

Ann: Yes, I was. I know I was.

Bob: And you couldn't tell anyone that. You couldn't tell him because he was winning over you again and you couldn't tell your mother.

Ann: No.

Bob: You couldn't, could you?

Ann: I wouldn't have even been able to describe how I was terrified.

Bob: But looking back, you could see that you were.

Ann: Yes.

Bob: And that is where this one is coming from.

Ann: I don't know.

Bob: It must be. It is the same deal. He's going to pin you down again. Someone is going to pin you down.

Ann: I don't know.

Bob: So your brother comes to you now and starts with this blanket thing again – what are you going to do? You are not going to resign, obviously. Are you going to run?

Ann: No, I would fight him off!

Bob: What would you say?

Ann: What the bloody hell do you think you are doing? Get lost! Get it off me!

Bob: Would you?

Ann: Yes.

Bob: You wouldn't have any doubts about that?

Ann: No, no my instinct would be to push him off.

Bob: Tell him to get lost?

Ann: Yeah. My instincts were doing then as a child. I was fighting him but obviously he was stronger and bigger and I didn't have much choice in the matter. But, you know, I don't know.

Bob: It's to do with the terror from there I'm sure. Can you see you are terrified then, but you couldn't at the time?

Ann: Yes I can. But no I couldn't verbalise I was terrified. I knew I was feeling it, but I had nowhere to go with it. And I didn't have any choice because I didn't have the back up from mum

Bob: So who were you angriest with then, your brother or your mother?

Ann: At the time I wasn't angry with either of them.

Bob: Quite. Who should you have been angry with?

Ann: More so, my mother.

Bob: I would have thought so. What's happened now, what feeling do you get?

Ann: It's been all part and parcel to everything else.

Bob: Is it still there?

Ann: What the anger?

Bob: Yes, the anger.

Ann: Well, I think about it sometimes, yeah.

Bob: Good well, tell me about it. What was your brother's name by the way?

Ann: Brian.

Bob: Brian. Go on then tell her about it. Sit her over there and say. . .

Ann: Um, what about the one particular incident?

Bob: Yes, "The blanket incident".

Ann: Um. That you weren't there to support me and you took my brother's side all the time. You should have been there for me to help me out to protect me. And I am pissed off that you failed as a mother.

Bob: How pissed off?

Ann: Really pissed off.

Bob: Are you? Very angry?

Ann: Not as angry as I used to be.

Bob: OK, but still angry?

Ann: Yeah, if I think about it, yes.

Bob: Because she didn't protect you.

Ann: Yes, she could've been a bloody better mother.

Bob: She could have protected you.

Ann: She could have done, yes.

Bob: You're going to start saying that nobody is protecting you.

Ann: Yes, that's right. No one is stopping my brother from behaving and doing what he wanted to me. It was never there, it was never stopped. Never.

Bob: Well your mother should have stopped it.

Ann: Sure.

Bob: So now you are going under general anaesthetic and nobody is protecting you under general anaesthetic.

Still struggling. I keep throwing out possible leads, to follow up – but despite both our best endeavours, they run into the sand. The point to emphasise is that Ann is as keen as I am to find where the root of the problem is. It's not failure of consent or cooperation on her part that is foiling us, it's the strength of her denial which uses all her mental stamina not to see. Quite a complex picture, difficult to describe, and easy to ridicule. The whole thing might be thought laughable, except for the prospect of her completely negating her complex medical treatment on the operating table on the morrow, or worse.

Ann: Hang on a second. I don't know if there is any bearing, I don't know . . . it's just come in. When I had my first, or went under the first time, because I was trying to think of a really bad experience first time around. Now my mother was with me the first time. I don't know if it's significant or not. But, while I was pregnant with Jane, I had to go in to have a Caesarean. I was 19, and it was a planned Caesarean and I went in, and my mother and my father took me in and it was just after midnight.

My father drove us there and my father sat in the car. He said, "See you later then, Ann." I said yeah, right see you dad. Went off in and he just sits in the car – the stupid git. My mum walked in with me, she dumps my suitcase there and she hangs about for a bit. They told me to get into this cubicle and get myself ready and everything and she goes to me, "Right! I'm off now." and I said oh, all right. She said, "I'll see you in the morning, then." I said "Yeah OK then." And it was so cold but I didn't feel it was cold, it was normal. She said, "I shall see you then", and I said, "All right." And I remember the nurse, saying to mum "Aren't you going to hang around until she goes under the anaesthetic and everything." My mum said "No she's all right. I'll see her tomorrow." So whether that plays something in there, I don't know!

Bob: Sounds good to me.

Ann: I don't know. I didn't feel it at the time, that it was terrifying or anything and when I went under the anaesthetic, I just felt very alone. I remember being alone.

Bob: Rejected again.

Ann: Yes. It was the norm, you know.

Bob: But you were angry?

Ann: No, I wasn't. That's the point. I wasn't angry about it.

Bob: You should have been.

Ann: I don't know, should I have needed her at 19 anyway?

Bob: Well no, that's not the deal. The nurse thought she could stay. You need someone there whether you are 20 or 100 or whatever.

Ann: Well yeah, I mean I was there for Jane but. . . Yeah, I guess, I don't know, I suppose because it was normal again. When I went under the anaesthetic, it was my first anaesthesia and when they put me under, I didn't know what to expect. I was just lying there waiting for it and they said oh you're going to go to sleep in a minute. I thought, "All right then." All of a sudden I felt it going through my body and the panic set in and I remember trying to sit up and they pushed me back down. And then I don't remember any more. That was the panic setting in then.

Bob: What was that panic about?

Ann: I think because I didn't know what was happening. I didn't know what to expect, or what was going on. How it was going to affect me, I guess.

Bob: But now you do, it's still not helping.

Ann: Yes, it hasn't helped.

Bob: This is all to do with your mother not protecting you. She didn't protect you against Brian.

Ann: No.

Bob: You may have some work to do on that. There is still a sense of anger there, not major stuff, but you should be angry with her, for not protecting you. You're certainly angry with her for not protecting you and assisting you when you had your Caesarean.

Ann: Yeah, I think I have never been angry at her for that. For not being with me when I went for the Caesarean. It became a joke. She actually laughed with me about it.

Bob: Afterwards?

Ann: Yes. I think a year down the line, I think it was mentioned how she was, she just walked in, "I'm going now Ann,". "Right. I'll see you then, mum." She laughed about it and said how matter of fact we were.

Bob: Did you think it was a good thing?

Ann: Yeah. But I didn't think, you know. There was no "I wish it had been different". There wasn't any of that in there, it was just, it was funny, wasn't it?

Bob: No. It wasn't.

Ann: It wasn't but, there was nothing there to make me feel to contradict that.

Bob: This time there wasn't, she wasn't protecting you. That's the thing, protection. Who do you think will protect you tomorrow?

Ann: Nobody. That's the point. I don't.
Bob: Well part of you does. Obviously, part of you says "Well nobody! Woo!" Bonk. You are either going to resign or run. Because you haven't got something that you think you need, or your emotions think you need, i.e.: protection of some sort. Probably maternal protection by the sound of it.

I'm still struggling somewhat – but there is more animation than there was. It seemed logical to retrace the first anaesthetic experience. After all, there was a panic then, doused by the injection. But I have to admit these are small pickings. I've had experience of this before, indeed we had an inkling of it with Louise earlier – the abusive parent is clung to, for 'protection'. What was actually happening here with Ann, was a variant on that, and a most intriguing one – a variant I met here for the first time. So seeking for wider avenues, I revert to the actual steps that will take place tomorrow. After all, Ann does this in her mind and can see the lethal panic occurring as if it were real – perhaps if we take it step by step, we can find a way out of what is otherwise proving an entirely unsatisfactory adventure.

Bob: OK, let's put it in a scenario. You come in tomorrow, you are sitting there. Here's your mum she's going to protect you now, she's going to look after you, she's going to stay all the way through and hold your hand. How would you react to that?
Ann: I'd say you are bloody joking. She has never done that in her life. I wouldn't believe you.
Bob: No, but we've got to get through your feelings some how. We're going to find the remedy for the panic, and the remedy of the panic is someone to protect you.
Ann: You know, Tom said to me, "Doesn't it help knowing I'll be there?" and I said no, it doesn't.
Bob: See! No, that's right! It's not him, it's somebody else.
Ann: That is what I am saying.
Bob: Who is it you want to protect you? Yes you do, it's in there, and it's in there.
Ann: Well logically, yes Mum, but it is not clicking.

Bob: No it won't click because you don't see where it is coming from.

Ann: But it's got to bloody click by tomorrow, or they will be darting me around the hospital. I don't know. If I could see that I wanted mum there when I first went in for my Caesarean. I could see that that is the link. You know, if I felt that I wanted her there then I could make that link now.

Bob: You weren't allowed to feel that you wanted her there then. Just as you laugh now when I suggest that she comes along now – a ludicrous thing. It wasn't ludicrous then, but that wasn't what was going on. What happened to you was that I mean it is all part of the same pattern. You have this heart to heart with Brian and then he rejects you, wont stand up against your mother. And in the background before that your mother should have protected you against Brian. She should have protected you against the anxieties of the first Caesarean.

Ann: I don't know, should she?

Bob: Well, you need somebody there. She walked in – and there you were, about to undergo a life-threatening operation, kind of thing. And she says, all right, you're on your own. Well you were. Would you do that for your grandmother for pity sake? So are you angry with her for not helping you then?

Ann: No, I'm not. That's the point, I'm not.

Bob: Should you be? You should, you weren't exactly in a strong position then.

Ann: I don't know Bob, I really don't know on that. I look at it and think, well, I am 19. I'm in a safe place anyway, and I don't need a parent.

Bob: No, I'm not talking about a parent. I'm talking about just someone to be there.

Still not solid enough. I'm trying to persuade her to swallow a dysfunctional relationship with Mum. But the truth is I'm failing. She bats away my suggestions without any of the heat that I am looking for. But this notion of someone being there as a 'protector' seems to be gaining some traction. It's not clear who the missing person might be – certainly Mum can't be readily shoehorned into the empty slot. And again, Ann is positively no help whatsoever in determining who else it might be. I just have to keep coming up with new ideas, new creations to try and fill the post. Ann has known me a number of years, and never doubts that I will. Over 20 years of experience of 'denials' gives me confidence too – though there is nothing yet, apart from the few glimmerings already mentioned, to sanction our eventual success.

Most significant of all, as the next comments show, is that her future husband Tom, comes nowhere. He doesn't even merit significant mention. Think of that. Here is Ann undergoing what she firmly believes is her last gasp on this earth, and the man she is about to marry carries no weight at all. Here is a glimpse at why so many marriages disappear into the great black hole of denial – the one misperceives the other, while struggling with a life and death battle that has not the least relevance to today, nor therefore to the help or otherwise that your nearest and dearest is there to offer.

Ann: Well the nurses were there.
Bob: Yes. Something is going on. You want protection tomorrow. That is what is going on. Tom doesn't, count poor lad.
Ann: No he doesn't. It could be anyone stood there you know?
Bob: But you're waiting for protection tomorrow.
Ann: But I don't feel I'm waiting for someone to protect me.
Bob: Well, first of all, let's agree to the logic of it. Do you feel that's the logic of it?
Ann: I am not sure.
Bob: You go in there and you are terrified. The terror comes from dying. Somebody is either going to kill you or not protect you from being killed. That is the basis of the terror. Now the only person who has come into the frame so far is your mother.
Ann: Yes. But the only person who used to protect me was my brother.
Bob: Oh I see.
Ann: If that helps.

"If that helps" she says. Here we have been struggling for a good half hour, and she tosses in the route to salvation, on a take it or leave it basis. "If that helps" indeed ! Lucky I've a flexible approach, else I might have missed the only available exit from this potentially disastrous emotional mire.

Bob: How did he protect you against your mother?

Ann: Um, well he didn't protect me from them, he was like my protector. He was in a way, my parent. He was the one who would talk with me, play with me, do things. Communicate with me.

Bob: Which they didn't do. He did assist you, but when he stopped assisting you, that hurt.

Ann: Yes.

Bob: OK, let's get your brother there tomorrow then.

Ann: It feels nice he came along.

Bob: There you go! There you go! Whoopee! Pay dirt! I should say. Tom comes along, and says "Can I help?" and you say, "Who the hell are you?" Then Brian comes along after all this hassle and you say "Oh Brian!" No, Yes?

At last we hit pay dirt. Tom remember, is her future husband, while Brian is her brother, the one who is currently estranged, and the only member of her family for whom her emotions are other than lukewarm. This is solid. This is hot. This is what I've been rummaging around for. Even so, it does not come out nice and easily. Ann still professes puzzlement, and nonchalance. But the tone has changed, the gate to the real emotions is now wide open, all I have to do is march into it three or four times, and the problem collapses. You can tell from the nonverbals that I am happy to express my relief. The emotions flood from me, just as they are about to do from Ann. And where I was trying to be masterful, for example in trying to squeeze Mum into the vacant post – here I'm confident, and there's no way I'm going to be deflected now.

Ann: It's nice he would come along.

145

Bob: Wow, whoopee!

Ann: But I don't feel like he's going . . . .

Bob: It doesn't matter if Tom comes along, Tom can come or not.

Ann: Yeah, it doesn't matter.

Bob: No. But it matters if Brian does. Say it! Say it!

Ann: Well, It doesn't matter.

Bob: Yes it does, yes it does. You're not getting off that easy. It matters if Brian comes along, say it.

Ann: It doesn't matter.

Bob: He's the only one that gets you to light up. Tom comes along – bugger all. Brian comes along, "Where are you Brian?" Oh!

Ann: No, I don't. I don't think that, I think it would be nice if he did.

Bob: Why is it nice if Tom comes along?

Ann: Because he is going to be there anyway.

Bob: Sorry. No dice for that one.

Ann: He should blooming be there anyway.

Bob: You just told me it doesn't matter. Which doesn't make sense, because you really know, on the bottom line, that Tom and you, that's the unit right? Fine, but that's not what your emotions are telling you. Your emotions are saying "Oh Brian, Oh!"

Ann: It would be. Oh, hang on let me think about this.

Bob: That's the idea.

Ann: OK, I have an emotion. I'm not sure what it is, but I am quite pleased if you say my brother turned up. Where-as if my mum and dad turned up, it's nothing.

Bob: That's right. We will dismiss them. If Brian turns up . . . There you go. What's this emotion?

Ann: Somebody cares.

Bob: Oh, I see. Any body in particular?

Ann: Well he cares.

Bob: Ah, I see. And what does that mean?

Ann: I don't know.

Bob: Tom doesn't care a thing, does he? Huh!

Ann: Well, it's just different, isn't it?

Bob: It really is and we have to find out why. Brian, who you haven't talked to for 10 bloody years, is more important emotionally than Tom you talked to 10 minutes ago. So, explain that. Off you go.

Ann: Well Tom's always been around, and Brian hasn't.

Bob: Ah! Why is Brian more important than Tom? Hey, that's a good question.

Ann: I don't know.

Bob: Well, I want to know.

Ann: I haven't got any answers on that one.

Bob: Oh yes you have!

Ann: Have I?

Bob: Yes. You're not leaving here until we get it.

Ann: I don't know.

Bob: You're the one on the spike. You say, Tom comes, yah, yah, yah. Brian comes, dilly, dilly, dilly, lights up. All the lights go on, Christmas tree, bang!

Ann: So what is he doing then, protecting me from my mum and dad?

Bob: Probably, something like that, he's protecting you from not existing, or something. We said before . . .

Ann: Flipping hell this is getting complicated.

Bob: No it isn't. It is very, very simple. He communicated with you where they didn't. And he allowed you to exist, where they didn't. So, you go into a situation where your existence is in the air, and he will reassure you.

Ann: He becomes the parent.

Bob: Yes, like he did before. Like I say, it wasn't your parents. "Brian used to protect me" is what you said. Then we went into a bit, apart from his torturing you, now and again. And he used to talk to you. Now that's a red herring, now we need to go into the positive side, because that is the danger side of this case. He used to talk to you, he used to communicate and he used to 'exist' me. That's what we decided right? He's more existing of you than your parents were.

This is a somewhat technical use of the verb 'exist'. I found that it has a transitive sense. Your parents give you your existence, or not. And the verb that fits this most neatly is 'they exist you', or at least they are the prime candidates for doing so. In this case of course, the exception comes to the fore – and it is Brian, a brother, not a parent who comes along to do the existing for Ann. Illegitimate existing, as it happens since Ann is now well capable of taking care of, and providing for her own existence on her own responsibility and authority.

Ann: Yes. He was always there, if there was danger.

Bob: There you go!!

Ann: Yes.

Bob: Ha, ha, ha.

Ann: At school, if there were problems at school, or if there were any boys that were being horrible to me, he would literally go and beat them up. And he would come back to me and say "I've sorted it for you, Ann".

Bob: So, he'd better hurry along tomorrow and say "I've sorted it for you, Ann" hadn't he?

Ann: What is he going to sort for me?

Bob: I don't care – but that is what you are waiting for. "Brian please sort it for me". Come on, sit him down and tell him.

Ann: Tell him what that he's going to sort it?

Bob: "I am in danger tomorrow, Brian, come and sort it please". Come on tell him.

Ann: Come and sort it for me tomorrow, because I am going to be in danger.

Bob: That's right. What happens to you when you say that?

Ann: Nothing, because I don't believe it. It is like I am asking him something that isn't true.

Bob: Well you're going into danger . . .

Ann: But, it's not, is it?

Bob: I know that. But your emotions are telling you its extremely dangerous. And every time you've gone into extreme danger before he's been there to sort it.

Ann: Yes.

Bob: Well, link those two.

Ann: So what I am going to do then?

Bob: I don't care. You want him to exist you like he did before, or go beat up the bullies at school. He was always there if there was any danger. There is danger tomorrow and he is not there. That is why you are panicking.

That's the kind of direct statement I prefer to make. It has taken rather longer than usual to arrive at it – but it would make the perfect 'homework' for Ann, should she need it. "If danger threatens, where's Brian?"

Ann: But he wasn't there when I went in for the Caesarean.

Bob: No, nor was your mum but you didn't know to panic until the injection was in your arm. You thought, "Wow!" and they held you down because you were well under way.

This is where he is, say it again, "He was always there if there was any danger," say that.

Ann: Yes, he always there if was any danger.

Bob: Say "There is danger tomorrow and he is going to be there". Say that.

Ann: There is danger tomorrow and he is going to be there.

Bob: That's right. And if he isn't, I am going to panic.

Ann: And if he isn't, I am going to panic.

Bob: That's right.

Ann: I don't know. I sort of buy it.

Bob: Good, which bit do you buy?

Ann: That he was there as the protector and was there for the danger side of things. I go along with that because he was. And even my mother used to tell him to look after me.

Bob: So that was the one time she took any interest in you at all?

Ann: Well, no. It wasn't. It was because she was pissed off with me worrying about something and she said go find your brother and let him sort it for you.

Bob: That's him being a parent.

Ann: Yes. And that is what she did. And I had to go off to my brother and my brother would go to mum and she would say to him "look just sort it out. You're there, I'm not, you sort it." And in the morning she'd say "right stick with your brother and he'll sort it for you". Ah, cheers mum.

Bob: And that's what you'll do tomorrow, stick to your brother. I like it.

Ann: I don't know. Why didn't I panic though in the first bloody Caesarean, when I went for the Caesarean before?

149

Bob: You didn't know. You didn't know you were going to be out of control. You walk up there, you turn there, and you go in the cubicle and everything's fine then ah! Bonk. This time, you don't want to go. You see the bloody needle going in the arm before they even start.

Ann: Because I'm fine up until I see the needle going in. I picture it, and I see the needle going in and think, "Right. That's it. Shit. I'm out of here!"

Bob: Danger – where's Brian. Go on, say it.

Ann: Right. There's danger, where's Brian?

Bob: That's right. How is that?

Ann: Don't know.

Bob: Danger, where's Brian? Say it again.

Ann: There's danger, where's Brian?

Bob: Yeah.

Ann: I'd said he'd fucked off, being scared.

Bob: Yes, this is what happened ten years ago when he stopped being your parent. And you felt . . . You may have felt that your existence was threatened at that time. You may say that your existence is being threatened tomorrow and he has got more power than Tom to intervene. That is classic irrational infant stuff.

Ann: It is. It is totally irrational.

Bob: It's not today's reality. It's yesterday's reality. And who is yesterday's reality? Clearly it is Brian.

Ann: Well it's certainly not mum and dad.

Bob: No. Absolutely. I buy that.

Ann: And the fact is that Brian used to protect me, so it's the only logical thing isn't it?

Bob: So should he protect you tomorrow? Picture it.

Ann: I can't. I can picture him there.

Bob: Good. Picture him there. What is he doing?

Ann: Nothing. He just stood there and that's all he ever bloody did do.

Bob: No he didn't, he beat up the bullies.

Ann: Yes. He did do, when he was younger. I don't know. I don't imagine him doing anything. I don't imagine him saying anything to anyone or even saying anything to me, because he was a very, very non-verbal person really.

Bob: Yes, he was there. He was always there if there was any danger.

Ann: Yes.

Bob: Say that again.

Ann: He was always there when there was any danger. Oh yeah, he did save my life a couple of times.

Bob: There you go.

Ann: We used to have a three-storey home and our bedrooms used to be on the top. Top floor and we used to look down the banisters, right the way down to the ground floor. And we used to play these stupid games on the banisters. And I had gone over and I couldn't get back up and I was hanging. And I remember screaming because I knew I was going to fall but he came out and pulled me over. And he always told me, don't tell mum and dad what you've done.

Bob: How old were you then?

Ann: Round about 8, 9. He said "Don't ever tell them". Because I remember him pulling me over and feeling him yanking me back and falling on the floor and crying because I knew I had gone that close, to dropping and he said, "Don't ever tell them."

Bob: Because?

Ann: Because I would've got it in the neck. He knew I would have taken a battering for it. So, you know, keep it to yourself.

Bob: And the other time?

Ann: The other time was when we were messing about again and we had run down one of the corridors. And we had like a rug, a long rug and I'd slipped. And at the end of the corridor, on the hall was a huge, big mirror, and I slipped and I don't know how it happened but the mirror came right down and smacked right on top of me, covered me totally. And, I don't know if it knocked me out or not, but I remember being a bit funny then. And he pulled me out from under the mirror and sat with me and made sure that I had come round properly and everything else. And he said again, don't you tell mum. Don't you say nothing. Because either he would get it in the neck, you see, or he'd watch me get it.

Bob: So he is going to be able to save you tomorrow? I'm very pleased about him saving you tomorrow.

Ann: I don't know, I don't know. It makes sense. It makes sense, but I don't feel.

Bob: Well, we will have to connect up your feelings to what makes sense.

Ann: I know they are not connecting.

Bob: I wonder why that is.

Ann: Why wouldn't they?

Bob: Because the fear around the whole rotten, stinking pathological childhood you have just come out of.

Ann: Possibly.

Bob: So what have we decided? Describe what we've decided. Tell me, "My panics come from . . .

Ann: My panic comes from my parents.

Bob: Tomorrow they come from?

Ann: Still my parents, because of the fear of death.

Bob: And?

Ann: But I am waiting for my brother to protect me from that, so I don't die.

Bob: Can you see that?

Ann: Well it makes sense. I can't see it, but it makes sense.

Bob: It came out very smoothly.

Ann: Yeah. Well, it makes sense, doesn't it?

Bob: Yes. It is like . . .

Ann: I can't say I believe that, because I can't feel it.

Bob: Ok, so what bit can you feel?

Ann: I know that, and I believe that I am going to die tomorrow.

Bob: What about believing your brother can protect you.

Ann: Yeah, he used to.

Bob: It is getting closer. He used to protect me. But he's not there anymore so no body can protect me. Say that?

Ann: Right. He is not there anymore, so no body can protect me.

Bob: That's right.

Ann: I don't need anyone there to protect me.

Bob: Oh! Your emotions are certainly telling you otherwise.

Ann: I know. And of course if he comes to the hospital, then it is a nice feeling that he is there. And I don't give a stuff if it's anyone else.

Bob: Brian gives nice feeling. Which is crap for pity's sake, but anyway it does. You've got to go over the feelings. Brian gives you nice feelings.

Ann: I don't know what that is.

Bob: I do.

Ann: What?

Bob: He is stepping into parental shoes.

Ann: He's being a parent again. Hmm. Which I should have had off of mum and dad.

Bob: Yes, these two incidents that you said, "Don't tell mum and dad – i.e. they aren't parents, and I am the parent." So, he was being parental then. Parents should save your life, he saved your life therefore, he is being parental. And that is what you want tomorrow, the nice feeling if he is there. That is the key. That's the key. So as the panic comes on, lets do it: put the needle in, and say Brian's around, and see what happens to the panic.

Ann: Ha. I'd be looking around to see where is he then?

Bob: That's right, what happens to the panic?

Ann: It doesn't go down, until I see him.

Here is the clearest statement so far. And it comes with full emotional backing. We have spent this long, looking for the key emotion behind the panics – and here we have it. The panics go down "when I see him", or rather not "until I see him". Hearing this, I knew that we had the right answer, I also knew that it was sufficiently near Ann's full consciousness that, with only a little encouragement, it would flourish. Our toils were all but over.

This takes on something of the appearance of a 'blurt', another technical term. What happens is that the 'real' feelings underneath have come so near to the surface, that they burst through, before the defensive 'denial' can stop them. They appear in the open air, without their logical clothing – before they can be rationalised away. And they point straight to the very heart of the emotional distress. They are not easy to engender – after all, they are a spontaneous bursting through of the denial defences. But when they arrive, you put out more flags – this is the key to unlock the lethal agonies that would otherwise descend. What you then need to do, is feed them straight back to the sufferer demanding to know what they meant when they said it. They cannot deny saying it, nor that it reflects a serious truth – this is the golden spanner for unlocking emotional hammerlocks.

Bob: Ha, you fell right into that one.
Ann: Well I'm waiting for it and I'm looking around for it.
Bob: It doesn't go down until I see him, and then it does.
Ann: Well I don't know, I didn't get that far.
Bob: It's your brother that you're looking for.
Ann: That is what I am looking for. . .
Bob: Course it is. Hey, that's good! Put that in a sentence.
Ann: Well I assume I am!
Bob: So do I! I've assumed it for the last 10 minutes. What are you looking for?
Ann: For my brother to protect me.
Bob: That's right . . . That's right. Say it again.
Ann: I am still picturing him being in there.
Bob: Good.
Ann: Yeah, yeah, it is. It's the safety. With him it's safety.
Bob: So put that in a sentence.
Ann: With my brother I feel safe and he is there to protect me. He stops me dying.
Bob: That's right. How useful.
Ann: How lovely.
Bob: He stops me dying.
Ann: Yeah. How the bloody hell am I going to get over this by tomorrow?
Bob: Easily. Just realise where you are.
Ann: I believe I need my brother to survive.
Bob: Yes, that's right, very good, very good.
Ann: And without him, I die.
Bob: That's right, that's right.
Ann: Right, which is crap.
Bob: Yes, but it has been there.
Ann: It's been there.
Bob: Still pulling your strings today.
Ann: Uh huh.
Bob: Tell Brian – "Please stop me dying."
Ann: Brian, please stop me dying. Yes, he is the only one who has been able to do that.

Bob: Ha!

Ann: Because if I said that to mum and dad, I automatically think "Well say it to mum and dad, and its just 'No'."

Bob: What about Tom? He doesn't fare too well poor sod. So we say it to Brian what happens to you?

Ann: There's an anticipation of waiting for it.

Bob: That's right and there's expectations that it'll work.

Ann: Yes.

Bob: The panic doesn't go until I see him and when I see him it goes. Because I have to wait till I see him. That is the answer to that. So what is the answer?

Ann: That I believe I need my brother to survive tomorrow, to stop me from dying. But I ain't going to die tomorrow am I?

Bob: I don't think you are going to die tomorrow, but part of you does.

Ann: Well it's the unknown, I suppose.

Bob: No. It's well known. The rejection, non-existence and you are dead. It's well known.

Ann: Yes. But that's nothing to do with anaesthetics is it?

Bob: Yes, it has been linked to the anaesthetics from the first experience of anaesthetics and your mother buggered off. And, it is covered and twisted, there is no question that Brian became parental, and still is today.

Ann: Yes, I can see that. Some elements are in there aren't they?

Bob: I'm afraid so.

Ann: I wonder what else he pulls?

Bob: That is all, that's all. You manage to escape from your parents non-existing you, manifestly. And the panics associated with that have gone. This is an extreme situation, which triggers a situation where you were helpless before. As it happens the last time it was with your mother – but now it is quite clearly your brother. He is always there if there is any danger. There is danger tomorrow, in your view or part of your view.

Ann: So how am I going to get rid of this one then?

Bob: Well you ask him to help. Sit him down.

Ann: Brian can you help me tomorrow? (Pause) Yeah?

Bob: What happens?

Ann: Well, two things going on. One side is waiting in anticipation of what is he going to do for me then. The other side is a complete sort of like absolute nonsense.

Bob: That's right and what has to happen is the nonsense has to win. And it isn't winning at the moment. Hello Brian, please stop me dying. Off you go...

Ann: It does, it's there isn't it? See because I believe you can.

Bob: Hurray! No wonder you couldn't unpack this yourself. Ho! What a clever doctor I am! Tee he! Tee he!

I have to add here, that this must be the first time I have indulged in such self-congratulatory hyperbole – it is really a sign of the desperation I had been feeling at the start, that I did not really have any idea of where these potentially lethal panics were coming from. And now that we've uncovered their root, and thereby cured them, I'm so relived I pat myself on the back rather more immodestly than usual.

Ann: You ought to start coming back to work.

Bob: Steady. I'm doing you so you can do this. "Hello Brian I need you, I need you to stop me dying."

Ann: I need you to stop me dying.

Bob: That's right. That is all you have to look at.

Ann: He gets up and says what do you want me to do?

Bob: No, he doesn't.

Ann: No, that's the two things that are going on.

Bob: Quite. The second one you go for. Hello Brian I need you to stop me dying. You need to get the need in. Stress the need. I need you to stop me dying. Say it again.

Ann: Brian, I need you to stop me dying.

Bob: That's it.

Ann: It's definitely that, isn't it? It is definitely half and half as well.

Bob: What's that? Oh, you mean the nonsense bit?

Ann: Yes.

Bob: Is absolutely rubbish but. . .

Ann: It is quite strong.

Bob: Which bit is quite strong?

Ann: The need for my brother.

Bob: Say it, verbalise that. Say I have a strong need for my brother to stop me dying . . . .

Ann: I have a strong need for my brother to stop me dying.

Bob: No, only . . How old are you? 40?

Ann: I am 39 and I think I need him to survive. Oh poor bugger.
Bob: Which is the poor bugger?
Ann: My brother. Ha, ha!
Bob: My feelings are with Tom as a matter of fact. You can see how it arises, everything's shut out, its tunnel vision.
Ann: Yes, it is. I've shut him right out of this, totally. I know what I've got to do. Get on and do it, and that's it. And it's like . . .
Bob: Something is telling you can't do it without Brian.
Ann: Yes, he's got to be there, be there waiting.
Bob: Say, I can't do this without you, Brian. Go on say it.
Ann: I can't do this without you, Brian.
Bob: I like that one. I like that one very much, say it again.
Ann: I can't do this without you, Brian. Yeah, it definitely plays in there doesn't it? So I've just got to get a load of reality in there tonight.
Bob: Get the reality in there now. Sit him down there and what are you going to say, Hello Brian . . . What are you going to say?
Ann: I don't need you to survive anymore, I am an adult.
Bob: Oh, who believes that?
Ann: Partly me. I think he'd believe it.
Bob: And partly, not you.

Here we can see the dogmas being exposed. Here Ann is being as honest, and as brave as Lenny was earlier. "Partly" – this covers the point exactly. Part of her does, and part of her doesn't. Before she did not know that this dilemma existed, she only knew the agonies of the terrors. Now we have the emotions pointing in two diametrically opposite directions – back to childhood, and forward to adult reality. Again, once you can reach this point, you are looking at the problem together, and it is just a matter of time before the pieces fall into place, the dogmas become fully exposed which leads inevitably to earlier obsolete terrors evaporating.

Bob: I don't think he would as a matter of fact. But you don't, do you.
Ann: No. Only partly with this.
Bob: Still homework, isn't it?

Ann: I will sit up all night tonight doing it.

Bob: Well, I wouldn't do that. What you have to do, is get a clearer picture of what the link still is, and a clearer picture of where the damage is, where the mud still is, if you like.

Ann: I wonder if it's tripped me up anywhere else then.

Bob: It doesn't matter; it's tripped you up for tomorrow. So you have to deal with that. Describe your situation. What have we uncovered? What have you got to do tomorrow?

Ann: That my fear of dying and the only one that can stop that is my brother. So I am saying that I need him to survive.

Bob: Good and what's your comment on that?

Ann: Well, I am not going to die anyway.

Bob: I am glad to hear that.

Ann: And having my brother there, is something I don't need today.

Bob: You don't?

Ann: As a child, I needed him.

Bob: Yes, some time ago.

Ann: But today as an adult, I don't need him.

Bob: Apart from what your emotions are telling you.

Ann: I know. At least I can see it now! I have something to work with now.

Bob: You have haven't you? Fascinating isn't it? I sat here, to begin with, thinking where the hell are they. I thought, "Stick with the rules". The rule is, it's panic, it's infant, it's this . . .

Ann: Yes. I know, and that is what bugged me, because I couldn't think where it was coming from.

Bob: Well you can't, because it's your wall.

Ann: That is why I said to you, I've got to see you. Because I knew there was something there, and I knew I couldn't work it out.

Bob: You couldn't work it out because it pays you not to work it out.

Ann: That is right, yeah. Pays me not to think it through, pays me not to see it, because it's a bloody lifeline isn't it?

Bob: You go down the normal passage, i.e. mum and dad, ludicrous that. But in the first introduction, Brian is torturing you, abusing you. But in fact, like I say the positive side, which is the most difficult side, you're clinging to Brian in case you don't exist, don't you? Say that.

Ann: I don't feel as if I'm clinging to him to exist. I need him to save me in case I don't.

Bob: Right. What happened 10 years ago, still hurts today. That he isolated you.

Ann: It doesn't hurt now. It's just very sad that he had to do that. And I understand why he has done it.

Bob: Well . .

Ann: When he did, I was very angry at him. I was really angry at him for doing that.

Bob: I thought there was a bit more to it, when you first said that. Angry with him, rejecting you, you said. Today you are angry with him. I mean that was the clue for me. I thought ,well hang on, there is some emotion there that shouldn't be there. I just sort of clocked it going by. I said "pay attention to Brian" type thing.

Ann: Yeah, I think a lot of it, I have worked out. But obviously there has been stuff that has been left. And I think, like, I was angry at him when he did reject me and he did walk away and push me out. I could really see I had been rejected then. Sort of spent a lot of time working on that. And I had to understand his point of view from where he was coming from, as he was in the same boat as me.

Bob: He still hurt you.

Ann: Yes, he did that. But he also hurt me looking at it now, more so, because he was my protector.

Bob: That's right. What I am saying is that as we were going along, that was a clue to me, to look at Brian that he was a protector there. And there was some residual emotion from you, for him today. Which shouldn't be there. He says "I don't want you" and you say "that's your choice, your loss."

Ann: Yes.

Bob: Ok, so what's your homework. What are you going to say?

Ann: I have to be really crystal clear on linking this – that it is him, that I feel I need to stop me dying tomorrow.

Bob: Can you tell Tom that?

Ann: Yes.

Bob: What will you say? Hello Tom . . .   Off you go.

Ann: Well, I have finally worked out what it is. That I realised I needed my brother with me tomorrow, so I don't die.

Bob: You said that "Good, I'll go get him." You know it's very curious this, I'm sitting here thinking "I can't hold her hand". And that's so wrong, and you could see what it was doing?

That was the pain that you were describing. And it was absolute agony, you were going there, and your protector wasn't there so all we had to do was to crystallise, clarify who your protector was. Could you have half a dozen of them, the nurses and stuff, Tom is clearly the man but he . . .

Ann: He cuts no ice. He wasn't the protector, I was looking for was he? And also to be quite honest, I don't really need one anyway.

Bob: I'm glad to hear that bit. I thought that bit all along, I don't mind someone comforting you.

Ann: I have been trying to get that in my head, all the time.

Bob: You can't do it, unless you see what your other part's doing.

Ann: I know.

Bob: So what's the rest of you been doing?

Ann: Been searching and waiting for my protector.

Bob: Name of?

Ann: My brother, Brian.

Bob: That's right. You can have a conversation, say – "Hello Brian I need you to survive". Go on, say that.

Ann: Hello Brian, I need you to survive.

Bob: That's a panic, if you don't.

Ann: And if you don't, I'll panic.

Bob: Yes, that's right.

Ann: Yeah, I can see it. It is like expecting him to protect me.

Bob: Panic doesn't go away until I see him, say that.

Ann: The panic doesn't go away until I see him. I know that's all becoming very clear. The fact is, I don't want that . . . I don't need that bit.

Bob: You don't actually have to have it. It's your choice. Are you happy wanting to have it?

Ann: Yes, I need to be crystal clear to see it, and then I can get rid of it.

Bob: So what's crystal clarity?

Ann: Oh, that I need my brother to protect me so I don't die.

Bob: That's right, that's true. The panic doesn't go down till I see him. That's gorgeous that is. That's what was blurred.

Ann: It is the expectation. It is there. And I suppose he did deliver as a child. He delivered that, and I suppose I am still waiting for that.

Bob: That's right. Exactly. That is all.

160

Ann: Shame my bloody parents weren't like that! Wasn't it?
Bob: You did very well. See you same time next week. It will all be over by then.
Ann: Yes. . . .
END OF TAPE

Is it my imagination, or was that a tiring exercise? I didn't mind being bereft of any clue, initially, as to the actual detail of where the lesion was, or where the fault line would be found. I had total confidence, as indeed did Ann, that the gross size of the impending deathly panic in the morning arose from a dysfunctional emotional survival system, of similar size. It's just that I'm used to finding them in the parental bondings, or partial parental bondings. It just goes to show, when dealing with the human mind, especially one that is suffering serious agonies, that dogma and inflexibility can cripple healing.

It also shows how invaluable this approach is. I find such explorations totally fascinating – there isn't another intellectual challenge that can compare. And the pay off, the outcome is quasi-miraculous. Happily Ann went through her operation the next day, totally unscathed. She no longer needed the support and protection her brother had offered her in the past. Only when she came up against a set of circumstances that mimicked her life threatening situations from before, were these panics precipitated. Had this not happened, then who knows, perhaps this issue might never have surfaced, or at least not surfaced so dramatically, nor so urgently. But having worked it through as above – these panics will never recur. Were they to poke their nose over the parapet, the response of "where's my brother to save my life" would draw Ann firmly into the present day, where protectors are real, and available, not unreal and unreliable as they were too often in her past.

What happened here shows how deeply damaging and dangerous these irrationalities can be. Every suicide is the cry of an infant for protection – but as we've seen that protection has to be of a very specific sort, and as like as not, one that would be entirely vacuous were it ever now to appear.

What the foregoing offers is a different approach, a different pathway through the tangles the human mind can knot itself into. Not an easy option, but a decidedly optimistic one. Which is why I love it so much. However, times move on, and I have recently taken the painful decision to close my clinic, so as to publish the data. I must stop doing, and start writing. Certainly had I not done so, then I could not have written this book at this time. I have decided I must close my clinic door – in the hope that I might persuade many others to open theirs. By no means an easy decision – but one which I hope will fructify elsewhere.

8) WHERE WE GO FROM HERE.

reality and insanity

Is reality so hard to get hold of? Surely it doesn't require a medical degree to grasp the fact that there is someplace out there where we move about, have breakfast, fall in and out of love, and eventually, not being immortal, die. "Humanity cannot stand too much reality" – well it had better learn sharpish, else there will be rather less reality around to understand. Darwin was certainly right about one thing – adapt, or die. And the thing we all need to adapt to, is reality out there – technically known as our environment.

Darwin emphasised the physical aspect – if you find yourself on dry land, you had better learn to breathe air pretty fast. If your territory keeps getting flooded, better learn to walk on two feet, so as to keep your head above water. But the same principle applies, if not more so, to the representation of that 'real' world, in our minds. And again, the same axiom applies – keep your mental model up to date, so you are adapting to what is real, or as near as we can make it. And the penalty, as before, even in small gradations, is – if you don't adapt, you die (a little or a lot, depending on circumstances).

So here is humanity's Achilles' heel. We have made unprecedented strides in evolutionary terms, outstripping all known rivals, at least for the present aeon and excepting possibly the insects. We do this by cooperating. We work together, more flexibly than ants. And we communicate, not only in the here and now, but with past wisdoms by the fabulous invention of the written word. But if our mental models become askew, if our communications become opaque, if our thinking ceases to be straightforward, then we risk becoming unrealistic. And being unreal in a hostile, entropy-spewing, anti-life world is intrinsically unhealthy. Darwin described the penalty, and it is ruthless, remorseless and unremitting.

No problem then, if we keep a clear head, making sure that what we think is happening out there, or going to happen, is as near as possible to what is. This is the pragmatic definition for Truth – does what you think or say, bear as close a resemblance to what is real as you can make it. Truth can never be 100% true, because we only have a mental symbol of the real world in our heads – we couldn't have the real thing – there isn't enough room. So we have to make do with a model, a picture – which by definition is not reality, and can never be, however 'scientific' we might become.

This leads smoothly on to a comprehensive definition of insanity – built as all things human tend to be, on a graduated scale, a seamless spectrum. Thus – the truer our mental pictures, the nearer we come to sanity. The reverse also applies.

From this, we can begin to draw up a straightforward aetiology, or cloud of causative factors which tend towards insanity, and away from mental health – quite a useful exercise one would think, if we wish for a safer, saner world. And the first thing to go wrong is errors of fact. We might believe, for example, that nuclear power is by far and away the cheapest, safest, least politically insecure source of energy for the next 20 years. But if this is not factually accurate, as I suspect it is not, then we would be mad to go down that route. It would take a long time, wagon loads of money, and leave vast headaches for posterity. We would be sacrificing our scope for adapting, and thereby restricting our capacity to survive. And the word 'mad' is technically correct, since insanity and unreality cohabit.

Errors of fact are closely followed by errors of belief. You may believe that when the last tree is cut down, Jesus Christ will appear. Now questions of belief, indeed of theology require careful handling. I am in no position to declare that what you believe is heresy, since we have spent the last millennium finding out the hard way that freedom of speech, of association and of thought is literally vital. Vital that is if we wish as a species, to retain flexibility in our battle for survival against an unfriendly cosmos. So I have no wish, nor happily any authority to brand what you believe as heretical. Equally, you must grant me the right to do the same. The views I hold are my own affair, I keep them in my mind, into which you may venture only if invited. Some of my beliefs I hold lightly, others with strenuous weight. You are at liberty to accept or reject any of these, as you see fit. The main belief I have with respect to the mind is, as already described, a robust antagonism to dogma. I don't like dogma. I see dogma damaging so many aspirations. If you will permit the solecism, I'm dogmatically against dogma. And that applies to mine as well as yours.

Errors of fact may be settled to a large extent by careful observation and dispassionate reasoning. Errors of belief can be remedied by cool discussion and persuasion. What remains is – errors by irrationality. And again, we have a pragmatic definition of irrationality. There are a myriad medical concepts which defy tight definition, pain is one, and health another – the tighter you tie them down, the flimsier they become. You and I know what pain is, we don't need any verbal definitions, nor, when we have it, any florid descriptions. Similarly with health – your definition of health may differ from mine – but when we have it, we both know it is a most enjoyable thing to have.

Now irrationality, which is the very core of psychiatry, has a much clearer definition than any of the foregoing. Irrationality is the application of a set of reasoning, a set of axioms, beliefs or dogmas that held true in the past, but do no longer. In the political sphere, it is irrational to suppose that the best way to combat terrorism is by wielding your own terror – wrong. The best way is to find the roots of terrorism, and methodically cut them. Slow it may be, prone to betrayals and to set backs – yet the way to a terrorist's mind is through the front door – talk. A dramatic military invasion may be so much easier to 'sell', especially with the ferocious application of an over-grown technology – but can only make sense if you prefer drama to success. Rationally it makes no sense to prefer war to peace.

Irrationality in psychiatry is the prolongation into adult life of beliefs and axioms learnt in childhood. These are not just any old beliefs – they are strategies for very survival. It is an evolutionary fact of life that all human infants are born paraplegic – they cannot move. If danger threatens, they are helpless. If they are not fed, they perish. They know this – and their emotions, which are essentially driving towards survival, keep them tightly attached to the relatively enormous adults around them. Fear of not surviving cements these early childhood patterns – melting that fear, allows adult behaviours and insights to prevail.

The human Achilles' heel is thus a two-fold adaptation– as human beings we are required to adapt not to one environment, but to two – very different ones. The first is when we arrive on this curious planet and survive or not, at the whim of others – the second is when we are adult, and offer survival to others, or not, on our own recognisances. Most make this transition effortlessly – but many do not. And the scope of the irrationalities that result has to be seen to be believed.

to my psychiatric colleagues (& everyone else)

I have set out in this book to challenge what I see as current psychiatric dogmas. I do so because I observe them to inflict more damage than benefit, promoting more iatrogenic disease and less healing. I have developed these notions over 50 years, and as a doctor I find them more beneficial than harmful. I do not offer them here as a new dogma to replace the old – but rather to encourage you to look more closely at those who seek your help, and find out if they are as true for you as they have proved to be for me.

During my varied career, I have met many different responses from my psychiatric colleagues. Sadly those in a position to advance my career have been more incensed than those not. On the other hand, the 'expulsions' that ensued have led me into paths I would not have otherwise travelled, and provided me with opportunities to learn, which would not normally have come my way. In particular I learnt the full extent of denial in general practice, which was the last destination I envisaged for myself as a medical student. And being evicted from six different consultant psychiatric posts, gave me a catholic experience, from 'psychopaths', to self-harmers, from anorexics to phobics – whence my current psychiatric confidence, and the simplicity and universality of the model I now pursue.

So the first point to clarify is – does mental health exist? And the second – does fear power the chief pathology of denial? As to the first – don't try and define what mental health is. There is no need to. When setting up my medical computing system in 1969, one of the axioms I needed to establish was what constituted a symptom. A symptom is defined by a patient walking into my consulting room and telling me about it. A man may have chest pain walking up and down the street, but if he seeks no medical assistance, then this does not fall within the medical realm. It remains a private personal matter – it is not a symptom as such, because it has never been brought to medical attention.

Similarly, what you might regard as mentally healthy, others may see as exotic – and very much vice versa. But if that person seeks your help, then this gives you the necessary permission to intercede. Then it falls to you to advise. It does not fall to you to take over the life of that person, nor to impose your dogmas on hers. This is essentially no different from any medical disease anywhere. The individual with the problem comes to their medical advisor seeking help to ameliorate that problem. It's just that with mental symptoms, which tend to be more frequent and more agonising, there are certain precepts it is prudent to observe

The primary point to remember, which was well driven home to me while working in Parkhurst Prison, is that doctors operate by consent. This is well established in surgical practices – but it is especially crucial in mental health. In general medicine you may offer a treatment to an individual – it is then up to that individual whether or not she consumes it. You may offer advice, such as stop smoking – but you don't do the stopping – they do, or not.

Consent is indispensable if progress towards better mental health is to be achieved. And this brings us to a more subtle point. One medical dogma I hear too often is that the person asking for help cannot ever be mentally healthy again. The point was discussed in an earlier chapter – it is crucial here. If as medical adviser, you really do not believe in your heart of hearts that there is any positive hope for that individual, if you remain utterly convinced that mental health will remain a dream – then you are not really the best person to provide medical succour for that individual, and you should say so.

Perhaps you have never experienced mental health yourself – perhaps you have only a vague idea of what it could possibly be. Well, either equip yourself with better understanding, or refer elsewhere. This is no different from any other speciality in medicine – you don't have to know everything from oncology to dermatology from endocrinology to neurology – but if you offer assistance to the mentally troubled, then you need to acquire the conviction that such assistance can make a material difference. In other words that mental health does exist, and that you can promote it, or at least offer fruitful advice towards that noble end.

The second question relates to denial, and to the fear which powers that. Again there is no need, indeed no chance, of defining what fear actually is, nor will there ever be any way of measuring it with any degree of accuracy. In this it is exactly equivalent to pain – for which no measuring device has ever proved successful, nor any definition meaningful.

As before, do not take this as a dogma to be learnt by rote, nor indeed to be rejected out of hand. Look afresh at your patients. Observe their emotions. Ask them if they have any fear, just as you would if they have any pain. Learn how to assess descriptions of fear, just as you learnt how to assess descriptions of pain. There is essentially no difference in the demands this places on clinical skill.

There is of course one major distinction between the role played by fear in medical practice and that played by pain. Few patients see any point in minimising or obscuring their pains – they come straight out with them, often too gushingly. With fear on the other hand, they will too often find the point so painful, so dangerous, they daren't even tell themselves, let alone you. Which leaves you rather in the dark, especially if you insist all discussion of emotions is outside your remit.

Again further training may be called for, to trace the buried terrors which power the pathology of denial. You will be well familiar with referred pain – that is pain arising in one organ, but felt only elsewhere. Cardiac pain 'referred' to down the arm, and felt there, not in the chest – this is the classic example. So with denial – this is referred fear. The items to which the fear attaches are not those from which it arises. Thus terror is transferred or 'referred' to shopping for example, or to eating, or to any of an infinite range of human thoughts and activities.

But the real root of the fear is not to be found there – it is to be found deeply hidden away from sight, below as thick levels of concrete and obscurity as that individual can muster. And it will remain so, unless you have the skill to provide a trustworthy enough context, with abundant confidence that the sufferer can find a way through, can 'pull themselves together' given adequate emotional support. You have to consent to them exploring these terrors – a lot to ask, if you've received no training there, nor had any experience. Dogmas from the past can seriously suffocate medical healing.

to talk therapists (& everyone else)

The central problem with talk therapy is – what to talk about? If you study Freud carefully, as I did in my first psychiatric career, then you find that prior to his father's death in October 1896, he talked as normally as you or I – indeed his paper written in April of that year on *The Aetiology of Hysteria* is as clear and relevant today as anything written since. However following his father's death, and his notorious letter to Fliess of 17 September 1897, in which even his own father (now unsafely deceased) would have to be criticised as being perverse, things fell apart. His metaphysics along with his recommended approaches disintegrated. I estimated that from 1900 when he insisted that dreams meant more than froth, through to 1938, he moved the goal posts every 5 years or so. Thus he glid from sex, to breast, to penis, to anus, to any part of the physical anatomy that looked as if it might shore up his disintegrating mental anatomy. He finally ended up with a 'life-death' instinct, a type of 'unmoved mover', with as much relevance to mental health as Old Moore's Almanac.

But the final nail in his coffin has been the rigidities with which too many of his more faithful acolytes now regale their customers. Freud was the talk therapist par excellence – he initiated the whole process. He paved the way for a new approach to mental health. Talking was his thing. He must be turning in his grave to hear accounts of hour upon hour spent in silence whereby 'classical' psychoanalysts sit mute while their clients say nothing. It's not only the blind leading the blind, but the deaf non-communicating with the deaf. Sounds like torture to me. Another expensive way of making things worse.

Following Freud's demise, a myriad of other talk therapies have sprung up, aided by the persistent refusal of DSM-psychiatrists to even consider emotions, let alone discuss them. Here, I would offer the same two axioms as to my psychiatric colleagues. First have a clear end point to your therapies – what are you aiming for, have you a goal towards which your endeavours and those of your customers is set? And secondly, be aware of the central role played by fear, and its pathological counterpart – denial.

Freud's lack of end points made a nonsense of his approach. The 'cure' for Oedipus was to marry his mother – not an exactly sane outcome to strive for. The end point that makes most sense to me is the eradication of childhood fears, which moves in tandem with the transfer from an infantile survival strategy, to an adult version of the same, which being more realistic, is thereby saner.

It would be as well to compile a list of the positive aspects of mental health which are freely available to every human who ever walked the planet. Self-confidence, self-esteem, a demonstrable ability to control the emotions, not them you – these are just a few of the foothills. But they represent the minimum. Every living soul is unique, with unique talents and abilities – they should feel self-assured, they should blossom, they should be in control of where they are, and where they want to go. Happiness is our birthright – we are a sociable species, and should not cease until we harvest it.

The transfer from childhood survival patterns to emotional maturity is not always smooth. Every therapist and indeed every recipient of therapy, should keep in mind the axiom *'parenting keeps infants alive, and adults insane'.* It should be obvious to both parties, and if it is not, should be constantly made so, that the emotional demands of an infant are grossly different from those of an adult. These differences are not minor, they are not hard to distinguish – they are as gross as the bodily size difference between the two stages of human development implies. The one is 100% dependent on parental or carer's approval – the other is interdependent and in charge; the former is initially 100% the responsibility of others, the latter 100% responsible for her or himself.

The bind is that every sufferer from uncontrolled irrational emotions is looking for an ideal parent to sort things out, rather as their original parent somehow failed to do. Pressures, sometimes enormous life threatening pressures, are applied to any who have, or appear to have authority or power – these pressures are directed towards supplying the emotional sufferer with a good parent. In fact the parenting of adults radically disempowers them, keeps them infantile, prolongs their suffering and cements in their minds the conviction that there is no escape from their unacknowledged but agonising childhood nightmares.

So every therapist should have a cut off point – the one that I recommend is where both parties agree that the emotional ties to the nursery have been severed. The sufferer no longer has one foot in the cradle. When this happens, all, and I mean all, symptoms evaporate, and the ex-sufferer can pick up their lives without fear or favour. If they do not, then as with Ann earlier, that means only one thing – there is more terror still left to uncover.

As before, the main drawback, the deepest pitfall is fear, and the denial it engenders. Of course the therapist must take all steps to ensure that *their* own parental remnants have been exposed to today's daylight, and are no longer lurking behind a sophisticated 'invisibility cloak' of denial. Bear in mind that each denial is different, just as every mind is unique, so the methods by which it disguises from itself those items and especially those emotions it does not want to see, are infinitely varied. There have been occasions when I have had to say to my customers – "Look, you are brighter and quicker than me. You have the evidence. I merely ask painful questions. If you keep running rings around me, then my capacity to assist is limited."

As mentioned in the dialogues which appear earlier, these are not normal conversations. Unless you centre the conversations on areas with which the individual before you is uncomfortable, then progress is unlikely. Nothing can be more soul-destroying than two individuals circling around each other, ad nauseam, each scrupulously avoiding the other's emotional blind-spot, while loudly proclaiming that neither has any.

I find nothing more fascinating than sniffing out areas of mental furniture that have been cordoned off – unaccountably. The sufferer themselves is generally most unhelpful in this regard, since it has always been their intention ever since childhood, to ensure that these 'taboo' areas are kept well away from full consciousness. So the part I enjoy is bouncing along, firing off questions at random, to see which bit sticks. All the while keeping a wary eye out for the slight delay in response, the marginal rise in tone, the wisp of emotion which disappears as soon as it flits by – all indicating that that part of the mental forest is out of bounds, is a 'no-go' area, is simply not up for discussion or public consideration. In other words, it is precisely there that the denial is in operation, and precisely there that all focus must be brought to bear – though, as always, with overt, explicit and fully informed consent.

Consent is clearly most crucial here. And it calls for a decidedly nice judgement. Looked at in the round, what we are asking the sufferer to do is to think things they have long deemed quite unthinkable, to answer questions which if asked in the kindergarten would automatically lead to annihilation or death, or its nearest infant-equivalent. And all this with the individual's explicit consent. For without that, there is no point starting – as before, they are in charge of their minds, they are the only one's who are, and if they cannot be persuaded to stop keeping part of them locked away in a leaky box, then that is the end of the matter.

The problem with all denied emotions, all no-go areas, is that the energy needed to maintain such unhelpful mental items is huge – the mind normally runs smoothly onwards, it takes unusually strong emotions to deflect it. What every sufferer therefore needs is a context, a setting with commensurately large amounts of trustworthy support, so that, over time and with every encouragement, they may be persuaded to open their mental boxes, review their infantile obsolete terrors, and ventilate them to the outside air.

In a sense, the overall process is one of validating their adult capabilities. It's not always easy to learn, there are so many pitfalls which entrap the unwary – but when it works, as work it will, the outcome is stunning. Watching the human mind blossom, while participating in it casting off nursery dross, is surely a wonder to behold. For myself, I have now closed all my clinical work – to give me time to write books such as the present one, and to prepare video training materials which display the process more obviously. But this does nothing to detract from the fascination that this success entails. After all this is the most intriguing, the most delightful entity in the entire cosmos, and to see it stretch its wings, escape the deadly bondage of a misspent infancy and then flourish – this verges on the miraculous.

towards a safer psychiatry

This book is now drawing to its close. It's origin was the persistent refusal of the bulk of the psychiatric profession to acknowledge the gaping hole that had appeared in its pharmaceutical armoury. At first, I thought it was such an important book to write that there must be someone better qualified to write it. However as I turned the matter over in my mind, a month ago, I gradually tumbled to the notion that I could write it. I am no expert on brain chemistry – but then there are many such experts, who have already described the details and the evidence better than I could, and more than adequately for any who care to read them. The case against the 'anti-psychotics' for example, which I prefer to label the 'pro-psychotics' is made lucidly enough by my friend Robert Whitaker, and his paper on the matter appears in the Appendix which follows next.

As I wrote the first chapter, and came to the second, it became increasingly obvious that persistently ignoring the drug evidence was merely one part of a larger problem, a problem I had been familiar with over many years – namely the ossification of psychiatry. Now here, I was on firmer ground. Part of the reason the psychiatric profession 'needed' to ignore the adverse drug evidence was because of the insane yearning it has for becoming a speciality that is as concrete and as physically based as say cardiology or orthopaedics. It was as if psychiatry was saying, "Don't take away our drugs, they are the only thing which keeps our profession going". As if, in other words, psychiatry has become addicted to the prescribing of medication to keep itself alive, and refuses adamantly to consider any programme of 're-habilitation'.

This would account for the unexpected reception my approach has received over the years. I had thought that if I demonstrated how to persuade anorexics to eat, as I did with

Kate in chapter 3, that psychiatrists struggling with this lethal disease would bite my hand off to know how to do it. If I demonstrated how to eliminate self-harm, then a similar enthusiasm would be shown. Further if this approach eliminated violence from a bunch of supposedly incurable, treatment-resistant 'psychopaths' – then I would have my work cut out rushing all over, setting up similar schemes to bring equal success elsewhere.

In the event, it was not so much my hand, but my career that was bitten off. "You must understand," a psychiatric colleague told me in 1999, "that you are damaged goods." So the more benign view I developed regarding the practice of psychiatry did not receive the encouragement let alone the endorsement from other members of my profession that I had hoped it would.

And yet, as I progressed through chapter 2, the holes that appeared in the psychiatric knowledge base grew wider and deeper. I had known about them for decades, but actually spending time describing them, and linking them to chapter and verse in the main psychiatric text brought them more fiercely into perspective. Chapter 3 gave more details of the sort of damage that is now commonplace, arising from a decidedly dysfunctional psychiatric practice.

But as with any irrational activity, the resolution does not lie in continually berating the individual who is at fault – it lies in gaining a measure of trust, and in gradually persuading that person that there are in fact better ways of resolving the problems they face. At the moment, they may seem insurmountable. However, if the psychiatric profession could respond to some of the suggestions offered here, it would find an excellent future for itself. It would not need to follow in the strictest detail what I have prescribed – it might find that rather embarrassing. But it must follow something equivalent, some other way of restoring humanity to what is currently an increasingly inhumane branch of medical practice.

As stated in the foreword, this is far from being an anti-psychiatry book – mental health, and the issues surrounding it, is indeed the most vital aspect of all medical practice. There is every reason to suppose that when the lessons of ossification are fully learnt, and the implications of coping directly with fear, with denial and with the software issues involved, this branch of medicine could flourish as never before.

It is no mere hyperbole to say that the mind is the most important organ in the human organism. All other physical diseases are influenced by it, from cancer to asthma, from heart disease to psoriasis. Stress, as I found myself saying in general practice, is a killer – which surely is meat to any psychiatrist. If psychiatry could once be placed on a firmer, more realistic footing, then these golden accolades could well become a commonplace – as it fully deserves. But it will never do so while it rummages around in brain minutiae and continues to assault cerebral enzymes with increasingly destructive chemicals.

So what can the general reader do about this situation? Well, firstly overcome the fear of psychiatry. These are just doctors whose calling leads them to treat mental diseases, rather than physical ones. Then next, act to make the issue of humane practice, indeed of Human Rights come to the fore. Human Rights are indeed therapeutic – choice, respect, consent – without these mental health cannot flourish. They are woefully absent in our mental hospitals, especially our maximum security mental hospitals. It is every citizen's duty to ensure that such rights are applied, and are seen to be applied in even the darkest corners of our democracies.

As I wrote in my review of *Mad In America,* as cited above, "*every psychiatrist should be compelled to read at least the preface, every year. And everyone else should then insist on them describing in writing, every year, what they're doing about it.*" So why not start doing this, with the psychiatrists in your neighbourhood. They are just as human as you or I. They need to face facts, just as you and I do. Governments love to control – they need to have their fingers taken out of this particular pie. They will not do so, unless public pressure 'guides' them powerfully enough.

Robert Whitaker points out that medicating dangerous schizophrenics may not be the best way to improve our security. Compulsory medication therefore may achieve the opposite of what is intended – so breaking faith with Human Rights, and exacerbating our social insecurity at the same time. These facts need to be brought into the public arena. They need to be debated, so that their impact on legislation can be facilitated. Clearly if current psychiatric practice is as full of holes as described here, then these need to be repaired. For only a healthier psychiatry can lead to a less violent, more secure society.

If this isn't the responsibility of every citizen everywhere, then whose is it?

◻   ◻   ◻   ◻

APPENDIX

This appendix starts with Robert Whitaker's paper on the 50 year record of doing more harm than good. Next follows my Lancet paper of 1998, which though it failed to pass editorial muster, is here included to give cheaper and verse to the discussion of DSM-IV above.

Following on, is a paper I wrote, unpublished, giving results from my work in Parkhurst Prison.

Legislation plays an ever sharper role in our lives – there is a belief among certain politicians, that writing a law helps. A paper for a Select Committee was an attempt to cast some daylight into this crowded arena.

Finally there is a limited book list, for those interested in further reading in this most vital subject.

The Case Against Antipsychotic Drugs: A 50-Year Record Of Doing More Harm Than Good

Robert Whitaker
19 Rockingham St.
Cambridge, MA 02139
617-499-4354
robert.b.whitaker@verizon.net

Abstract: Although the standard of care in developed countries is to maintain schizophrenia patients on neuroleptics, this practice is not supported by the 50-year research record for the drugs. A critical review reveals that this paradigm of care worsens long-term outcomes, at least in the aggregate, and that 40 percent or more of all schizophrenia patients would fare better if they were not so medicated. Evidence-based care would require the selective use of antipsychotics, based on two principles: (a) No immediate neuroleptisation of first-episode patients; (b) Every patient stabilized on neuroleptics should be given an opportunity to gradually withdraw from them. This model would dramatically increase recovery rates and decrease the percentage of patients who become chronically ill.

The standard of care for schizophrenia calls for patients to be maintained indefinitely on antipsychotic drugs. The evidence for this practice comes from research showing the drugs are effective in treating acute psychotic symptoms and in preventing relapse.[1,2] Historians also argue that the introduction of neuroleptics in the 1950s made it possible to empty the mental hospitals, and that this is further proof of the drugs' merits.[3] Yet, long-term outcomes with schizophrenia remain poor, and may be no better than they were 100 years ago, when water therapies and fresh air were the treatment of the day.[4,5,6,7]

There is an evident paradox in the research record. The efficacy of neuroleptics appears to be well established, yet there is a lack of evidence showing that these drugs have improved patients' lives over the long-term. That paradox recently stirred an unusual editorial in *European Psychiatry*, which posed this question: "After fifty years of neuroleptic drugs, are we able to answer the following simple question: Are neuroleptics effective in treating schizophrenia?"[8] A close review of the research literature provides a surprising answer. The preponderance of evidence shows that the current standard of care—continual medication therapy for all patients so diagnosed—does more harm than good.

Did Neuroleptics Enable Deinstutionalization?

The belief that the introduction of chlorpromazine, marketed in the U.S. as Thorazine, made it possible to empty state hospitals stems from research by Brill and Patton. In the early 1960s, they reported that the patient census at state mental hospitals in the U.S. declined from 558,600 in 1955 to 528,800 in 1961. Although they didn't compare discharge rates for drug-treated versus placebo-treated patients, they nevertheless concluded that neuroleptics must have played a role in the decline since it coincided with their introduction. The fact that the two occurred at the same time was seen as the proof. [9, 10]

However, there were obvious confounding factors. In the early 1950s, the Council of State Governments in the U.S. urged the federal government to share the fiscal burden of caring for the mentally ill, and proposed that "out-patient clinics should be extended and other community resources developed to care for persons in need of help, but not of hospitalization." [11, 12] As part of this agenda, states began developing community care initiatives, funneling the mentally ill into nursing homes and halfway houses. This change in social policy could easily have been responsible for the slight drop in patient numbers observed by Brill and Patton.

Moreover, there was one state that did compare discharge rates for schizophrenia patients treated with and without drugs, and its results do not support the historical claim made for neuroleptics. In a study of 1,413 first-episode male schizophrenics admitted to California hospitals in 1956 and 1957, researchers found that "drug-treated patients tend to have longer periods of hospitalization . . . furthermore, the hospitals wherein a higher percentage of first-admission schizophrenic patients are treated with these drugs tend to have somewhat higher retention rates for this group as a whole." In short, the California investigators determined that neuroleptics, rather than speed patients' return to the community, apparently *hindered* recovery. [13]

The true period of deinstitutionalization in the U.S. was from 1963 to the late 1970s, the exodus of patients driven by social and fiscal policies. In 1963, federal government began picking up some of the costs of care for the mentally ill not in state institutions, and two years later, Medicare and Medicaid legislation increased federal funding for care of mental patients provided they were not housed in state hospitals. Naturally, states responded by discharging their hospital patients to private nursing homes and shelters. In 1972, an amendment to the Social Security act authorized disability payments to the mentally ill, which accelerated the transfer of hospitalized patients into private facilities. As a result of these changes in *fiscal* policies, the number of patients in state mental hospitals dropped from 504,600 to 153,544 over a 15-year period (1963-1978). [14]

Establishing Efficacy: The Pivotal NIMH Trial

The study that is still cited today as proving the efficacy of neuroleptics for curbing acute episodes of schizophrenia was a nine-hospital trial of 344 patients conducted by the National Institute of Mental Health in the early 1960s. At the end of six weeks, 75% percent of the drug-treated patients were "much improved" or "very much improved" compared to 23% of the placebo patients. The researchers concluded that neuroleptics should no longer be considered mere "tranquilizers" but "antischizophrenic" agents. A magic bullet had apparently been found for this devastating disorder.[1]

However, three years later, the NIMH researchers reported on one-year outcomes for the patients. Much to their surprise, they found that "patients who received placebo treatment were less likely to be rehospitalized than those who received any of the three active phenothiazines."[15] This result raised an unsettling possibility: While the drugs were effective over the short-term, perhaps they made people more biologically vulnerable to psychosis over the long run, and thus the higher rehospitalization rates at the end of one year.

The NIMH Withdrawal Studies

In the wake of that disturbing report, the NIMH conducted two medication-withdrawal studies. In each one, relapse rates *rose* in correlation with neuroleptic dosage before withdrawal. In the two trials, only seven percent of patients who were on placebo relapsed during the following six months. Twenty-three percent of the patients on less than 300 mg. of chlorpromazine daily relapsed following drug withdrawal; this rate climbed to 54% for those receiving 300 to 500 mg. and to 65% for patients taking more than 500 mg. The researchers concluded: "Relapse was found to be significantly related to the dose of the tranquilizing medication the patient was receiving before he was put on placebo—the higher the dose, the greater the probability of relapse."[16]

Once more, the results suggested that neuroleptics increased the patients' biological vulnerability to psychosis. Other reports soon deepened this suspicion. Even when patients reliably took their medications, relapse was common, and researchers reported in 1976 that it appeared that "relapse during drug administration is greater in severity than when no drugs are given."[17] A retrospective study by Bockoven also indicated that the drugs were making patients chronically ill. He reported that 45 percent of patients treated at Boston Psychopathic Hospital in 1947 with a progressive model of care did not relapse in the five years following discharge, and that 76 percent were successfully living in the community at the end of that follow-up period. In contrast, only 31 percent of patients treated in 1967 with neuroleptics at a community health center remained relapse-free over the next five years, and as a group they were much more "socially dependent"—on welfare and needing other forms of support—than those in the 1947 cohort.[18]

Drug Treatment Versus Experimental Forms of Care

With debate over the merits of neuroleptics rising, the NIMH revisited the question of whether newly admitted schizophrenia patients could be successfully treated without drugs. There were three NIMH-funded studies conducted during the 1970s that examined this possibility, and in each instance, the newly admitted patients treated without drugs did better than those treated in a conventional manner. [FN1]

[FN1] In the early 1960s, May conducted a study that compared five forms of treatment: drug, ECT, psychotherapy, psychotherapy plus drug, and mileu therapy. Over the short-term, the drug-treated patients did best. As a result, it came to be cited as proof that schizophrenia patients could not be

In 1977, Carpenter reported that only 35% of the nonmedicated patients in his study relapsed within a year after discharge, compared to 45 percent of those treated with neuroleptics. The non-medicated patients also suffered less from depression, blunted emotions, and retarded movements.[20] A year later, Rappaport reported that in a trial of eighty young male schizophrenics admitted to a state hospital, only 27% of patients treated without neuroleptics relapsed in the three years following discharge, compared to 62% of the medicated group.[21] The final study came from Mosher, head of schizophrenia research at the NIMH. In 1979, he reported that patients who were treated without neuroleptics in an experimental home staffed by nonprofessionals had lower relapse rates over a two-year period than a control group treated with drugs in a hospital. As in the other studies, Mosher reported that the patients treated without drugs were the better functioning group as well.[22, 23]

The three studies all pointed to the same conclusion: Exposure to neuroleptics increased the long-term incidence of relapse. Carpenter's group defined the conundrum

> There is no question that, once patients are placed on medication, they are less vulnerable to relapse if maintained on neuroleptics. But what if these patients had never been treated with drugs to begin with? . . . We raise the possibility that antipsychotic medication may make some schizophrenic patients more vulnerable to future relapse than would be the case in the natural course of the illness.[20]

In the late 1970s, two physicians at McGill University in Montreal, Guy Chouinard and Barry Jones, offered a biological explanation for why this was so. The brain responds to neuroleptics—which block 70% to 90% of all D_2 dopamine receptors in the brain—as though they are a pathological insult. To compensate, dopaminergic brain cells increase the density of their D_2 receptors by 30 percent or more. The brain is now "supersensitive" to dopamine, and this neurotransmitter is thought to be a mediator of psychosis. The person has become more biologically vulnerable to psychosis and is at particularly high risk of severe relapse should he or she abruptly quit taking the drugs. The two Canadian researchers concluded:

> Neuroleptics can produce a dopamine supersensitivity that leads to both dyskinetic and psychotic symptoms. An implication is that the tendency toward psychotic relapse in a patient who has developed such a supersensitivity is determined by more than just the normal course of the illness . . . the need for continued neuroleptic treatment may itself be drug induced.[24, 25]

---

treated with psychotherapy. However, the long-term results told a more nuanced story. Fifty-nine percent of patients initially treated with mileu therapy but no drugs were successfully discharged in the initial study period, and this group "functioned over the follow-up (period) at least as well, if not better, than the successes from the other treatments." Thus, the May study suggested that a majority of first-episode patients would fare best over the long-term if initially treated with "mileu therapy" rather than drugs.[19]

Together, the various studies painted a compelling picture of how neuroleptics shifted outcomes away from recovery. Bockoven's retrospective and the other experiments all suggested that with minimal or no exposure to neuroleptics, at least 40% of people who suffered a psychotic break and were diagnosed with schizophrenia wouldn't relapse after leaving the hospital, and perhaps as many as 65% would function fairly well over the long-term. However, once first-episode patients were treated with neuroleptics, a different fate awaited them. Their brains would undergo drug-induced changes that would increase their biological vulnerability to psychosis, and this would increase the likelihood that they would become chronically ill.

The World Health Organization Studies

In 1969, the World Health Organization initiated a study to compare outcomes for schizophrenia in "developed" countries with outcomes in "undeveloped" countries. Once again, the results were surprising. Patients in the three poor countries—India, Nigeria and Colombia—were doing dramatically better at two-year and five-year follow-ups than patients in the U.S. and four other developed countries. They were more likely to be fully recovered and faring well in society—"an exceptionally good social outcome characterized these patients," the WHO researchers wrote—and only a small minority had become chronically sick. At five years, about 64 percent of the patients in the poor countries were asymptomatic and functioning well. In contrast only 18 percent of patients in the rich countries were in this best-outcomes category. The difference in outcomes was such that the WHO researchers concluded living in a developed nation was a "strong predictor" that a schizophrenic patient would never fully recover.[26]

These findings naturally stung psychiatrists in the U.S. and other rich countries. Faced with such dismal results, many argued the WHO study was flawed and that a number of the patients in the poor countries must not have been schizophrenic but ill with a milder form of psychosis. With that criticism in mind, the WHO conducted a study that compared two-year outcomes in 10 countries, and it focused on first-episode schizophrenics all diagnosed by Western criteria. The results were the same. "The findings of a better outcome of patients in developing countries was confirmed," the WHO investigators wrote. In the poor countries, 63% of schizophrenics had good outcomes. Only slightly more than one-third became chronically ill. In the rich countries, the ratio of good-to-bad outcomes was almost precisely the reverse. Only 37% had good outcomes, and the remaining patients didn't fare so well.[27]

The WHO investigators did not identify a cause for the stark disparity in outcomes. However, they did note there was a difference in the medical care that was provided. Doctors in the poor countries generally did not keep their patients on neuroleptics, while doctors in the rich countries did. In the poor countries, only 16 percent of the patients were maintained on neuroleptics. In the developed countries, 61 percent of the patients were kept on such drugs.

Once again, the research record told the same story. In the WHO studies, there was a correlation between use of the medications on a continual basis and poor long-term outcomes.

MRI Studies

While most researchers have used MRIs to investigate possible causes of schizophrenia, a small number have employed this technology to study the effects of neuroleptics on the brain. These investigators have found that the drugs cause atrophy of the cerebral cortex and an enlargement of the basal ganglia.[28, 29, 30] Moreover, researchers at the University of Pennsylvania reported in 1998 that the drug-induced enlargement of the basal ganglia is "associated with greater severity of both negative and positive symptoms."[31] In other words, they found that the drugs cause changes in the brain associated with a *worsening* of the very symptoms the drugs are supposed to alleviate.

Relapse Studies:

As discussed earlier, evidence for the efficacy of neuroleptics is stated to be two-fold. First, the NIMH trial in the 1960s found that neuroleptics are more effective than placebo in curbing acute episodes of psychosis. Second, the drugs have been shown to prevent relapse. In 1995, Gilbert reviewed 66 relapse studies, involving 4,365 patients, and summed up the collective evidence: Fifty-three percent of patients withdrawn from neuroleptics relapsed within ten months, versus 16 percent of those maintained on the drugs. "The efficacy of these medications in reducing the risk of psychotic relapse has been well documented," she wrote.[2]

At first glance, this conclusion seems to contradict the research showing that the drugs made patients chronically ill. There is an answer to this puzzle however, and it is a revealing one. The studies by Rappaport, Mosher and Carpenter involved patients who, at the start of the experiment, were not on neuroleptics but were then treated either with placebo or a neuroleptic. And in those studies, relapse rates were lower for the placebo group. In contrast, the 66 studies reviewed by Gilbert were *drug-withdrawal* studies. In the studies she analyzed, patients who had been stabilized on neuroleptics were divided into two cohorts: One would keep on taking the drugs and the other would not, and the studies reliably found that people withdrawn from their neuroleptics were more likely to become sick again.

Thus, the literature suggests that relapse rates fall into three groups: lowest for those not placed on neuroleptics in the first place, higher for those who take the drugs continuously, and highest of all for those withdrawn from the drugs. Yet even that picture is misleading.

First, for the most part, the drug-withdrawal studies were conducted in a select group of "good responders" to neuroleptics, rather than in the general patient population. In the real world, up to 30 percent of hospitalized patients don't respond to neuroleptics. Among those who do and are discharged, more than one-third relapse within the next 12 months and need to be rehospitalized, even though they reliably take their medications. Thus, fewer than 50% of people who suffer a schizophrenic break respond to standard neuroleptics and remain relapse-free for as long as a year, but the relapse studies, to a large degree, were conducted in this group of good responders. In 1998, Hogarty pointed out how this study design led to a mistaken understanding of true relapse rates with antipsychotics: "A reappraisal of the literature suggests a 1-year, post-hospital, relapse rate of 40 percent on medication, and a substantially higher rate among patients who live in stressful environments, rather than earlier estimates of 16 percent."[32]

At the same time, the relapse studies were designed in ways that exaggerated the risk of relapse in the drug-withdrawn groups. In response to Gilbert, Baldessarini reanalyzed the same 66 studies, only he divided the drug-withdrawn cohort into "abrupt-withdrawal" and "gradual-withdrawal" groups. He determined that the relapse rate in the abruptly withdrawn group was *three times higher* than in the gradual group.[33] In other words, it was the abrupt cessation that caused much of the excess relapse risk. Indeed, in a further review of the relapse literature, Baldessarini found that only one-third of schizophrenia patients gradually withdrawn from their drugs relapsed within six months and that those who reached this six-month point without become sick again had a good chance of remaining well indefinitely. "The later risk of relapsing was remarkably limited," he concluded.[34]

The relapse studies are cited to support a paradigm of care that emphasizes continual drug therapy for schizophrenia patients. But upon closer examination, a new picture emerges. The real-world first-year relapse rate for patients maintained on neuroleptics is understood to be 40%, while the rate for patients gradually withdrawn from the drugs is 33%. Thus, once bad trial design is eliminated, the evidence for continual medication disappears. At the same time, evidence appears showing that a majority of patients—two-thirds in the gradual withdrawal studies—can do fairly well without the drugs.

Doing More Harm Than Good

Although this review of neuroleptics may seem surprising, the research record actually is quite consistent. The pivotal NIMH study in the early 1960s found that the drugs had a short-term benefit, but that over the long-term the drug-treated patients had higher relapse rates. Similarly, in his retrospective study, Bockoven found that patients treated with neuroleptics were more likely to become chronically ill. The experiments by Carpenter, Mosher, and Rappaport all showed higher relapse rates for drug-treated patients, and in 1979, Canadian investigators put together a biological explanation for why this would be so. The World Health Organization (WHO) reported higher recovery rates in poor countries where patients weren't regularly maintained on the drugs. Finally, the MRI studies by investigators at the University of Pennsylvania confirmed the problem of drug-induced chronicity in a compelling way. The drug treatment caused a pathological change in the brain associated with a worsening of symptoms—that is a convincing example of cause and effect.

Thus, there is a preponderance of evidence showing that standard neuroleptics, over the long-term, increase the likelihood that a person will become chronically ill. This outcome is particularly problematic when one considers that the drugs also cause a wide range of troubling side effects, including neuroleptic malignant syndrome, Parkinsonian symptoms, and tardive dyskinesia. Patients maintained on standard neuroleptics also have to worry about blindness, fatal blood clots, heat stroke, swollen breasts, leaking breasts, impotence, obesity, sexual dysfunction, blood disorders, painful skin rashes, seizures, diabetes, and early death.[35, 36, 37, 38, 39, 40]

Once all these factors are considered, it is hard to conclude that standard neuroleptics are therapeutically neutral. Instead, the research record shows harm done, and the record is consistent across nearly 50 years of research. [See "Timeline to Failure" in appendix.]

A Better Model: The Selective Use of Neuroleptics

At the very least, this history argues that the best model of care would involve selective use of neuroleptics. The goal would be to minimize their use. Several investigators in Europe have developed programs based on that goal, and in every instance they have reported good results. In Switzerland, Ciompi established a house modeled on Mosher's Soteria Project, and in 1992 he concluded that first-episode patients treated with no or very low doses of medication "demonstrated significantly better results" than patients treated conventionally.[41] In Sweden, Cullberg reported that 55% of first-episode patients treated in an experimental program were successfully off neuroleptics at the end of three years, and the others were being maintained on extremely low doses of chlorpromazine. Moreover, patients treated in this manner spent fewer days in the hospital than conventionally treated patients during the follow-up period.[42, 43] Lehtinen and his colleagues in Finland now have five-year results from a study that involved treating first-episode patients without neuroleptics for the initial three weeks and then initiating drug treatment only when "absolutely necessary." At the end of five years, 37% of the experimental group had never been exposed to neuroleptics, and 88% had never been rehospitalized during the two-to-five-year follow-up period.[44, 45]

Those results are much better than any achieved in the U.S. following the standard model of continual medication. Indeed, in his meta-analysis of such experimental studies, John Bola at the University of Southern California concluded that most "show better long-term outcomes for the unmedicated subjects."[23]

The Atypicals: Dawn of a New Era?

Admittedly, the record of poor long-term results reviewed here was produced by standard neuroleptics. The poor outcomes may also reflect prescribing practices in the U.S. that, until the late 1980s, involved putting patients on high dosages. The long-term research record for clozapine and other atypicals like risperidone and olanzapine has yet to be written.

One hopes that these newer drugs will lead to better outcomes, but there are reasons to be skeptical. As is now widely acknowledged, the clinical trials of the atypicals were biased by design against the old ones, and thus there is no compelling evidence that the new ones are truly better.[46] While the risk of tardive dyskinesia may be reduced with the atypicals, they bring their own set of new problems, such as an increased risk of obesity, hyperglycemia, diabetes, and pancreatitis.[47, 48, 49] Together, these side effects raise the concern that the atypicals regularly induce metabolic dysfunction of some kind, and thus their long-term use will lead to early death. The atypicals also have been shown to cause an increase in D2 receptors, just like the old ones do, and that is believed to be the mechanism that makes medicated patients more biologically vulnerable to psychosis.[50]

Summary

The history of medicine is replete with examples of therapies that were eagerly embraced for a period and then later discarded as harmful. A scientific examination of the evidence is supposed to save us from such folly today. And science has in fact provided research data to guide prescribing practices. The evidence consistently reveals that maintaining all schizophrenia patients on antipsychotics produces poor long-term outcomes, and that there is a large group of patients—at least 40% of all people so diagnosed—who would do better if they were never exposed to neuroleptics, or, in the alternative, were encouraged to gradually withdraw from the drugs. (The percentage of patients diagnosed with schizoaffective disorder, or some milder form of psychosis, that could do well without the drugs is undoubtedly much higher.)

This conclusion is not a new one, either. Nearly 25 years ago, Jonathan Cole, one of the pioneering figures in psychopharmacology, published a paper provocatively titled "Maintenance Antipsychotic Therapy: Is the Cure Worse than the Disease?" After reviewing the research data, he concluded that "an attempt should be made to determine the feasibility of drug discontinuance in every patient."[17] The evidence supported a standard of care that involved gradual withdrawal. The research record of neuroleptics since that time—most notably the WHO studies and the MRI study by investigators at the University of Pennsylvania—confirms the wisdom of his advice.

Indeed, Harding's long-term study shows that gradual withdrawal is an essential step on the path to full recovery. She found that one-third of the schizophrenia patients on the back wards of a Vermont state hospital in the 1950s were completely recovered thirty years later, and that this group shared one characteristic: all had long since stopped taking neuroleptics.[51] She concluded that it was a "myth" that patients must be on medication all their lives, and that in "reality it may be a small percentage who need medication indefinitely."[52]

Yet, in spite of all this evidence, today there is almost no discussion within psychiatry of adopting practices that would involve using neuroleptics in a selective manner, and that would integrate gradual withdrawal into the standard of care. Instead, psychiatry is moving in the opposite direction and prescribing antipsychotics to an ever larger patient population, including those said simply to be "at risk" of developing schizophrenia. While this expansion of the use of antipsychotics serves obvious financial interests, it is treatment that is certain to harm many.

Robert Whitaker's Appendix

A Timeline for Neuroleptics

Preclinical

1883	Phenothiazines developed as synthetic dyes.
1934	USDA develops phenothiazines as insecticide.
1949	Phenothiazines shown to hinder rope-climbing abilities in rats.
1950	Rhone Poulenc synthesizes chlorpromazine, a phenothiazine, for use as an anesthetic.

Clinical History/Standard Neuroleptics

1954	Chlorpromazine, marketed in the U.S. as Thorazine, found to induce symptoms of Parkinson's disease.
1955	Chlorpromazine said to induce symptoms similar to encephalitis lethargica.
1959	First reports of permanent motor dysfunction linked to neuroleptics, later named tardive dyskinesia.
1960	French physicians describe a potentially fatal toxic reaction to neuroleptics, later named neuroleptic malignant syndrome.
1962	California Mental Hygiene Department determines that chlorpromazine and other neuroleptics prolong hospitalization.
1963	Six-week NIMH collaborative study concludes that neuroleptics are safe and effective "antischizophrenic" drugs.
1964	Neuroleptics found to impair learning in animals and humans.
1965	One-year followup of NIMH collaborative study finds drug-treated patients more likely than placebo patients to be rehospitalized.
1968	In a drug withdrawal study, the NIMH finds that relapse rates rise in direct relation to dosage. The higher the dosage that patients are on before withdrawal, the higher the relapse rate.
1972	Tardive dyskinesia is said to resemble Huntington's disease, or "postencephalitic brain damage."
1974	Boston researchers report that relapse rates were lower in pre-neuroleptic era, and that drug-treated patients are more likely to be socially dependent.
1977	A NIMH study that randomizes schizophrenia patients into drug and non-drug arms reports that only 35% of the non-medicated patients relapsed within a year after discharge, compared to 45% of those treated with medication.

1978	California investigator Maurice Rappaport reports markedly superior three-year outcomes for patients treated without neuroleptics. Only 27% of the drug-free patients relapsed in the three years following discharge, compared to 62% of the medicated patients.
1978	Canadian researchers describe drug-induced changes in the brain that make a patient more vulnerable to relapse, which they dub "neuroleptic induced supersensitive psychosis."
1978	Neuroleptics found to cause 10% cellular loss in brains of rats.
1979	Prevalence of tardive dyskinesia in drug-treated patients is reported to range from 24% to 56%.
1979	Tardive dyskinesia found to be associated with cognitive impairment.
1979	Loren Mosher, chief of schizophrenia studies at the NIMH, reports superior one-year and two-year outcomes for Soteria patients treated without neuroleptics.
1980	NIMH researchers find an increase in "blunted effect" and "emotional withdrawal" in drug-treated patients who don't relapse, and that neuroleptics do not improve "social and role performance" in non-relapsers.
1982	Anticholinergic medications used to treat Parkinsonian symptoms induced by neuroleptics reported to cause cognitive impairment.
1985	Drug-induced akathisia is linked to suicide.
1985	Case reports link drug-induced akathisia to violent homicides.
1987	Tardive dyskinesia is linked to worsening of negative symptoms, gait difficulties, speech impairment, psychosocial deterioration, and memory deficits. They conclude it may be both a "motor and dementing disorder."
1992	World Health Organization reports that schizophrenia outcomes are much superior in poor countries, where only 16% of patients are kept continuously on neuroleptics. The WHO concludes that living in a developed nation is a "strong predictor" that a patient will never fully recover.
1992	Researchers acknowledge that neuroleptics cause a recognizable pathology, which they name neuroleptic induced deficit syndrome. In addition to Parkinson's, akathisia, blunted emotions and tardive dyskinesia, patients treated with neuroleptics suffer from an increased incidence of blindness, fatal blood clots, arrhythmia, heat stroke, swollen breasts, leaking breasts, impotence, obesity, sexual dysfunction, blood disorders, skin rashes, seizures, and early death.
1994	Neuroleptics found to cause an increase in the volume of the caudate region in the brain.
1994	Harvard investigators report that schizophrenia outcomes in the U.S. appear to have worsened over past 20 years, and are now no better than in first decades of 20th century.

| 1995 | "Real world" relapse rates for schizophrenia patients treated with neuroleptics said to be above 80% in the two years following hospital discharge, which is much higher than in pre-neuroleptic era. |

| 1995 | "Quality of life" in drug-treated patients reported to be "very poor." |

| 1998 | MRI studies show that neuroleptics cause hypertrophy of the caudate, putamen and thalamus, with the increase "associated with *greater* severity of both negative and positive symptoms." |

| 1998 | Neuroleptic use is found to be associated with atrophy of cerebral cortex. |

| 1998 | Harvard researchers conclude that "oxidative stress" may be the process by which neuroleptics cause neuronal damage in the brain. |

| 1998 | Treatment with two or more neuroleptics is found to increase risk of early death. |

| 2000 | Neuroleptics linked to fatal blood clots |

| 2003 | Atypicals linked to an increased risk of obesity, hyperglycemia, diabetes, and pancreatitis. |

References

1. Cole J, Klerman G, Goldberg S, and the National Institute of Mental Health Psychopharmacology Service Center Collaborative Study Group. Phenothiazine treatment in acute schizophrenia. Archives of General Psychiatry 1964; 10:246-261.
2. Gilbert P, Harris M, McAdams L, Jeste D. Neuroleptic withdrawal in schizophrenic patients. Archives of General Psychiatry 1995; 52:173-188.
3. Shorter E. A History of Psychiatry. New York: John Wiley and Sons; 1997. p. 255.
4. Hegarty J, Baldessarini R, Tohen M, Waternaux C. One hundred years of schizophrenia: a meta-analysis of the outcome literature. American Journal of Psychiatry 1994; 151:1409-16.
5. Holden, C. Deconstructing schizophrenia. Science 2003; 299:333-335.
6. Weiden, P, Aquila R, Standard J. Atypical antipsychotic drugs and long-term outcome in schizophrenia. Journal of Clinical Psychiatry 1996; 57, suppl 11:53-60.
7. Harvey P. Cognitive impairment in schizophrenia: its characteristics and implications. Psychiatric Annals 1999; 29:657-660.
8. Stip E. Happy birthday neuroleptics! 50 years later: la folie du doute. Eur Psychiatry 2002 May; 17(3):115-9.
9. Brill H, Patton, R. Analysis of population reduction in New York State mental hospitals during the first four years of large scale therapy with psychotropic drugs. American Journal of Psychiatry 1959; 116:495-508.
10. Brill H, Patton R. Clinical-statistical analysis of population changes in New York State mental hospitals since introduction of psychotropic drugs. American Journal of Psychiatry 1962; 119:20-35.
11. Council of State Governments. The Mental Health Programs of the Forty-eight States. Chicago: The Council, 1950. p 4-13.
12. Rusk, H. States map a new attack to combat mental illness. New York Times, February 21, 1954. p. 4-13.

13. Epstein L, Morgan R., Reynolds L. An approach to the effect of ataraxic drugs on hospital release rates. American Journal of Psychiatry 1962; 119: 36-47.

14. Scull A. Decarceration: Community Treatment and the Deviant, A Radical View. New Brunswick, New Jersey: Rutgers University Press; 1984.

15. Schooler N, Goldberg S, Boothe H, Cole J. One year after discharge: community adjustment of schizophrenic patients. American Journal of Psychiatry 1967; 123: 986-995.

16. Prien R, Levine J, Switalski R. Discontinuation of chemotherapy for chronic schizophrenics. Hospital and Community Psychiatry 1971; 22: 20-23.

17. Gardos G, Cole J. Maintenance antipsychotic therapy: is the cure worse than the disease? American Journal of Psychiatry 1977; 133:32-36.

18. Bockoven J, Solomon H. Comparison of two five-year follow-up studies: 1947 to 1952 and 1967 to 1972. American Journal of Psychiatry 1975; 132: 796-801.

19. May P, Tuma A, Dixon W. Schizophrenia: a follow-up study of the results of five forms of treatment. Archives of General Psychiatry 1981; 38: 776-784.

20. Carpenter W, McGlashan, T, Strauss, J. The treatment of acute schizophrenia without drugs: an investigation of some current assumptions. American Journal of Psychiatry 1977; 134: 14-20.

21. Rappaport M, Hopkins H, Hall K, Belleza T, Silverman J. Are there schizophrenics for whom drugs may be unnecessary or contraindicated? International Pharmacopsychiatry 1978; 13: 100-111.

22. Mathews S, Roper M, Mosher L, Menn A. A non-neuroleptic treatment for schizophrenia: analysis of the two-year postdischarge risk of relapse. Schizophrenia Bulletin 1979; 5: 322-332.

23. Bola J, Mosher L. Treatment of acute psychosis without neuroleptics: two-year outcomes from the Soteria Project. The Journal of Nervous and Mental Disease 2003; 191:219-229.

24. Chouinard G, Jones B, Annable L. Neuroleptic-induced supersensitivity psychosis. American Journal of Psychiatry 1978; 135: 1409-1410;

25. Chouinard G, Jones B. Neuroleptic-induced supersensitivity psychosis: clinical and pharmacologic characteristics. American Journal of Psychiatry 1980; 137:16-20.

26. Leff J, Sartorius N, Korten A, Ernberg G. The International Pilot Study of Schizophrenia: five-year follow-up findings. Psychological Medicine 1992; 22:131-145.

27. Jablensky A, Sartorius N, Ernberg G., Ansker M, Korten A, Cooper J, et al. Schizophrenia: manifestations, incidence and course in different cultures, A World Health Organization ten-country study. Psychological Medicine 1992; monograph suppl. 20:1-95.

28. Gur R, Cowell P, Turetsky B, Gallacher F, Cannon T, Bilker W, et al. A follow-up magnetic resonance imaging study of schizophrenia. Archives of General Psychiatry 1998; 55:145-152.

29. Chakos M, Lieberman J, Bilder R, Borenstein M, Lerner G, Bogerts B, et al. Increase in caudate nuclei volumes of first-episode schizophrenic patients taking antipsychotic drugs. American Journal of Psychiatry 1994; 151:1430-1436;

30. Madsen A, Keiding A, Karle A, Esbjerg S, Hemmingsen R. Neuroleptics in progressive structural brain abnormalities in psychiatric illness. The Lancet 1998; 352:784-785.

31. Gur R, Maany V, Mozley D, Swanson C, Bilker W, Gur R. Subcortical MRI volumes in neuroleptic-naïve and treated patients with schizophrenia. American Journal of Psychiatry 1998; 155:1711-1717.

32. Hogarty G, Ulrich R. The Limitations of antipsychotic medication on schizophrenia relapse and adjustment and the contributions of psychosocial treatment. Journal of Psychiatric Research 1998; 32:243-50.

33. Baldessarini R, Viguera A. Neuroleptic withdrawal in schizophrenic patients. Archives of General Psychiatry 1995; 52:189-191.

34. Viguera A, Baldessarini R, Hegarty J, Van Kammen D, Tohen M. Clinical Risk Following Abrupt and Gradual Withdrawal of Maintenance Neuroleptic Treatment. Archives of General Psychiatry 1997; 54:49-55.

35. T. Lewander. Neuroleptics and the neuroleptic-induced deficit syndrome. Acta Psychiatrica Scandinavica 1994; 89, suppl. 380:8-13;

36. Keefe R, Bollini A, Silva S. Do novel antipsychotics improve cognition? A report of a meta-analysis. Psychiatric Annals 1999; 29:623-629;

37. Arana G. An overview of side effects caused by typical antipsychotics. Journal of Clinical Psychiatry 2000; 61, suppl. 8:5-13;

38. Kane J, Freeman H. Towards more effective antipsychotic treatment. British Journal of Psychiatry 1994; 165, suppl. 25:22-31;

39. Glazer, W. Review of incidence studies of tardive dyskinesia associated with atypical antipsychotics. Journal of Clinical Psychiatry 2000; 61, suppl. 4 (2000), 15-20;

40. William Glazer, "Expected incidence of tardive dyskinesia associated with atypical antipsychotics," Journal of Clinical Psychiatry 2000, 61, suppl. 4:21-25.

41. Ciompi L, Dauwalder H, Maier C, Aebi E., Trutsch K, Kupper, Z, Rutishauser, C. The Pilot Project Soteria Berne. British Journal of Psychiatry 1992; 161 (suppl. 18): 145-153.

42. Cullberg J. Integrating psychosocial therapy and low dose medical treatment in a total material of first episode psychotic patients compared to treatment as usual: A three-year followup. Medical Archives 1999; 53:167-170;

43. Cullberg J. One-year outcome in first episode psychosis patients in the Swedish Parachute Project. Acta Psychiatrica Scandinavica 2002; 106:276-285.

44. Lehtinen v., Aaltonen J, Koffert T, Rakkolainen V, and Syvalahti E. Two-year outcome in first-episode psychosis treated according to an integrated model. Is immediate neuroleptisation always needed? European Psychiatry 2000; 15:312-320;

45. Lehtinen K. Finnish needs-adapted project: 5-year outcomes. *World Psychiatric Association International Congress*. Madrid, Spain, 2001.

46. Geddes J, Freemantle N, Harrison P, Bebbington P. Atypical antipsychotics in the treatment of schizophrenia: systematic overview and meta-regression analysis. British Medical Journal 2000; 321:1371-1376.

47. Liebzeit K, Markowitz J, Caley C. New onset diabetes and atypical antipsychotics. European Neuropsychopharmacology 2001; 11:25-32;

48. Erica Goode, "Schizophrenia drugs may raise diabetes risk, study says," *New York Times*, August 25, 2003;

49. Erica Goode, "Pancreatitis risk seen in schizophrenia drugs," *New York Times*, September 2, 2003.

50. Silvestri S, Seeman M, Negrete J, Houle S, Shammi C, Remington G, et al. Increased dopamine d2 receptor binding after long-term treatment with antipsychotics in humans: a clinical PET study. Psychopharmacology 2000; 152:174-180.

51. McGuire P. New hope for people with schizophrenia. APA Monitor 2000; Vol. 31, number 2. Accessed at: apa.org/monitor/feb00/schizophrenia.html.

52. Harding C, Zahniser J. Empirical correction of seven myths about schizophrenia with implications for treatment. Acta Psychiatr Scand 1994; 90 (suppl 384):140-146.

This paper appeared in the journal – Ethical Human Psychology and Psychiatry, Volume 7, Number 1, Spring 2005.

Contemporary Psychiatric Anomalies –
aetiology, emotion, mind & intent

article submitted to The Lancet 1998

etiolated aetiology

Aetiology is the key to medical acuity – without clarity as to causative factors, medical practice struggles to keep ahead of old wives' tales and populist nostrums. Attributing malaria to 'bad air' was our best guess, before microscopes could show us mosquitoes' entrails. Without electron microscopy, AIDS would devastate in utter medical silence, as Alzheimer's does. Opacity in aetiology strangulates therapeutics.

Contemporary psychiatry argues quite the opposite. Being *"neutral with respect to theories of etiology"* is an *"important methodological innovation"* according to the *Diagnostic and Statistical Manual of Mental Disorders* [1] (DSM-IV). More, DSM-IV declares that *". . a diagnosis does not carry any necessary implications regarding the causes of the individual's mental disorder. . . Inclusion of a disorder . . does not require that there be knowledge about its etiology"* [2]. Indeed, whereas the first edition of DSM *"reflected Adolf Meyer's . . . view that mental disorders represented reactions of the personality to psychological, social and biological factors,"* which seems eminently practicable, later editions deliberately *"eliminated the term* reaction*"* [3].

"The crisis in psychiatry" was the subject of a recent Lancet editorial [4], which, together with its unhelpful correspondence [4,5,6,7,8], touches on a crisis that is dire in the extreme. Three points on aetiology. Firstly, DSM-IV breaches its own claim to aetiological neutrality, by desperately hankering to return psychiatry to the organic medical fold. Muttering obscurely that 'mind/body dualism' is *"a reductionistic anachronism"*, it tries shamelessly to ditch even the term "Mental Disorders", while obfuscating that *"there is much 'physical' in 'mental' disorders"* [9]. Worse – *"The term 'organic mental disorder' is no longer used in DSM-IV because it incorrectly implies that the other mental disorders do not have a biological basis"* [10]. Something as obviously non-biological as *"death of a loved one"*, is arbitrarily excluded [11] (see below).

Secondly, summarily excommunicating Adolf Meyer without due process betrays Freud's malignant shadow. Like some sectarian Anti-Christ, Freud has divided psychiatrists for 100 years. During my 40 years, excess sexuality never once proved pathological. Freud was a clinical colossus, but his flaws were equally vast. 'Infantile Sexuality' – a conceit he dreamt up to exculpate his own father [12] – is a toxic abomination, poisoning our understanding of child abuse, even today.

Thirdly, medicine's saving virtue is its insistence that empirical clinical data invariably take precedence over any text – "listen to the patient", said Osler "[s]he is telling you the diagnosis". Empirically, *"death of a loved one"* tops every sensible stress scale, inflicts untold morbidity, while illuminating Attachment Theory. DSM-IV eliminates it, on the unclinical grounds that it is *"merely an expectable . . response"*. How sad if such incompetent reasoning lead to clinical incompetence, and from there, however indirectly, to malpractice.

emotionless nosologies

While it may just be possible if lamentable, to proceed as if aetiology were discardable, the same cannot be said for emotions. It is simply clinically impossible to describe mental diseases without them. Emotion features larger in mental illhealth, than pain does in physical – a fact no amount of ideological baggage can gainsay. Indeed the clinical descriptions in DSM-IV are replete with emotions (including *'worries'*) – its preamble and glossaries however, are mute.

DSM-IV perhaps unsurprisingly, declines to grasp the nettle of the fundamental nature of emotions. Emotions after all, are elusive, amorphous, utterly subjective, highly resistant to description, and 100% impervious to objective definition – a taxonomist's nightmare. Yet pain, which is equally subjective and intangible, has been competently dealt with by the medical profession for millennia. The key with pain, is not to argue endlessly about what it 'is' – but to become familiar with it clinically, to learn by clinical practice to distinguish between say dull and colicky pains, and having learnt, to hone one's perception by extensive hands-on experience. Precisely the same applies to emotions. There are subtleties and intricacies which must be observed with emotions – 'denial' and other emotional blind-spots can mislead, as can 'referred pain' – but given training and support, a fruitful clinical understanding can be acquired.

DSM-IV's hazards become obvious if the term 'anxiety' is replaced by 'pain', something it closely resembles in a mental context. 'Generalised Anxiety Disorder' would then be transliterated as 'Generalised Pain Disorder'. Some patients do complain of 'pains all over', but to offer this as a diagnosis invites clinical ridicule. Surely psychiatrists deserve better.

Worse, 'emotionless nosologies' become so unreal that the scope for iatrogenic disease is huge. Who would classify general medical patients into those with mild pain who whimper, and those with severe pain who 'cry out', the former resembling anxiety states, the latter psychoses. Self evidently, most pains are transitory – likewise anxieties and psychoses are episodic. To label a person for life a 'colic', just because she once had this symptom would be a travesty of clinical practice – so why do so with psychosis ?

Even more bizarre would be to divide patients by whether their pain was in the arm, or the leg. Medical staff at Ashworth Maximum Security Hospital follow a similar extraordinary logic by housing their patients in 'Mental Illness' or 'Personality Disorder' wards – a triumph of presumption over acumen. Once diagnostic categorisation ceases to be harnessed to therapeutics, more sinister purposes emerge – rigid diagnostic unchangeability may comfort doctors, but harm patients.

The mind is the most elastic, fluid and adaptable organ imaginable – humanity's crowning glory, which psychiatric nosologies can either celebrate or suffocate. For myself, DSM-IV's taxonomy needs inverting – emotions being placed centrally, not peripherally. Two emotions suffice – fear and anger, with their pathological variants terror and rage. One or both occur in every case, and bring a consistent therapeutic strategy and a repeatability to my everyday psychiatric practice that DSM-IV would find hard to credit. Personality Disorder it then transpires is 'your mind stopping you doing what you want'.

pull yourself together

As if aetiology and emotion were not enough to sink the contemporary psychiatric ship, there are still two further intractables to go – mind and intent. People in general assume they have a mind, they behave as if they do, and expect others to do the same – in what other organ do mental diseases occur ? Unhappily the mind is intangible and no objective evidence for its existence can be found, either in the world at large, nor in DSM-IV (as above), nor yet in the *British Journal of Psychiatry*, where it commands one paper in 10 years, apart from Prince Charles [13] who also bewails psychiatry's glaring anomalies. Intent is unmentionable (as are terror and rage). Must intangible philosophies always deflect barber surgeons ? Shouldn't psychiatrists really discuss consciousness more than anaesthetists ?

The mind in reality, is the most complex entity in the entire cosmos, with a higher content of 'unknowability' than anything else we are ever likely to meet. Though this deters DSM-IV, Freud to his credit embraced both mind and emotion. What sank Freud was intent. Like many of our contemporaries, he lived in a Deterministic Clock Work Universe, where Free Will was a mirage, and "pulling yourself together" about as feasible as jumping up and down so as to fly.

Intent is the real joker in today's philosophical pack – how can you define something that then intentionally alters itself ? Small wonder it is taboo throughout Academic Science. Yet this is an issue larger than one recalcitrant psychiatrist protesting for the curability of paedophilia and psychopathy – it brings psychiatry into conflict first with the law, and then with the fundamentals of democracy.

Legal practice collapses without the concept of intent – when you picked up that spade, did you intend to dig or to kill ? And democracy, especially one based on 'market forces' i.e. consumer choice, is utterly reliant on the electorate making its intentions known. All convinced democrats believe passionately in human rights and electoral choice and intention – little knowing how mortifying this is for contemporary psychiatry, for psychoanalysis and for too many academics.

Early in my five years at Parkhurst Prison, three murderers expressed their intent to kill me – risk assessment with a personal edge. Through Emotional Education, and by actively deploying the concepts of Truth Trust and Consent, their intent was re-directed towards more civilised, responsible, adult purposes. Uniquely in any Maximum Security Prison Wing they later reported that no alarm bells were rung for two years [14]. It is absurd to attempt risk assessment while ignoring intentions. It helps to find that under every frozen terror exists a personality yearning (and 'intending') to be sociable, lovable, and non-violent [15].

Evidence based medicine takes on a different hue when linked to democratic procedures. If every psychiatric customer was asked "would you like help to pull yourself together ?" – and the answer was 100% affirmative – then in a real democracy, psychiatry would have to work out how to deliver this. The omens are not good. The Royal College of Psychiatrists welcomed my work enthusiastically at their annual conference in 1995, but then did nothing to prevent its premature closure, firstly at Parkhurst in 1996, and now at Ashworth [16] [17]. We risk entering the third millennium in as much psychiatric ignorance as we entered the previous two.

=====================

Dr Bob Johnson   1500 words

formerly–Head of Therapy, Ashworth Maximum Security Hospital, Liverpool

References

1 Diagnostic and statistical manual of mental disorders, 4th edition, American Psychiatric Association, Washington DC. 1994. (DSM-IV); xix.
2 Ibid; xxiii.
3 ibid; xvii.
4 Editorial. The crisis in psychiatry. Lancet 1997; 349: 965.
5 Jones I. The crisis in psychiatry Lancet, 1997; 349: 1550.
6 Venegas RF. Loc cit.
7 Pincus HA. Loc cit.
8 Forshall S. ibid; 349: 1550-1551.
9 DSM-IV; xxi.
10 ibid; 10.
11 ibid; xxi.
12 Freud S, (1897) Letter dated September 21, in The Complete Letters of Sigmund Freud to Wilhelm Fliess, 1887 -1904, Trans Masson J.M. 1985, Cambridge MA, Belknap Harvard.
13 Prince Charles, 150th Anniversary Lecture.Brit. J Psychiatry (1991), 159: 763-768.
14 Report on HM Parkhurst Prison by HM Chief Inspector of Prisons,ISBN 1 85893 382 X, Home Office, 50 Queen Anne's Gate, London SW1H 9AT. 1995; 34: 3.12.
15 Panorama: Predators, BBCtv documentary transmitted 3rd March 1997
16 Russell Jenkins, "Doctors raise fears over top mental hospital". The Times, 17 April 1998:9
17 Rowden, Ray, "Sadly, there are too many doctors who are third rate". The Guardian, 13 May 1998,G2 6-7.

Lancet letter – Ashworth: The Horrors of Misdiagnosis

CORRESPONDENCE

Sir—Overfilling the petrol tank when the battery is flat, is both futile and dangerous—faulty diagnosis incurs wasteful often destructive therapy. Without a better diagnosis of its grievous pathology the horrors of Ashworth must inevitably worsen. The Fallon inquiry, the Secretary of State Frank Dobson, and your Jan 23 editorial [1] all miss the point. Hilary Hodge and myself in early 1998 represented imaginative management-sponsored endeavours to improve clinical care. The 15 consultant psychiatrists showed their managerial power by having us both removed even while Fallon was still conducting his inquiry. [2,3] Management reform without psychiatric reform is costly folly.

The month before I took up the post of Head of Therapy at Ashworth, which had been specially created to reflect my experience and expertise, the Medical Advisory Group noted in their minutes that "Dr Johnson's is not a medical appointment". It was only when the so-called treatment-resistant patients insisted on attending every group session, as did the Head of Psychology herself, that the consultant staff cited General Medical Council guidelines and the Mental Health Acts to expel me. The consultants deflected patients from the very door of the group therapy sessions, denying them entrance. These are the untreatable personality disorders. Dame Fiona Caldicott was called in to arbitrate and had no difficulty finding in the consultants' favour, untroubled by either the patients' views or my own.

Ashworth psychiatrists are not alone in misdiagnosing all mental disease—contemporary psychiatry takes its cue from DSM-IV, bizarrely presuming, against all the evidence, that social and emotional stress, even the death of a loved one, have no impact on mental disease. The horrors from this misdiagnosis exceed even those from the Ashworth variety—and are harder to remedy, given the level of support for it among government departments and medical editors.

Bob Johnson

1 Editorial. The horrors of Ashworth. *Lancet* 1999; 353: 251.
2 Jenkins R. Doctors raise fears over top mental hospital. *The Times* April 17, 1998: 9.
3 Rowden R. Sadly, there are too many doctors who are third rate. *The Guardian,* May 13, 1998: G2 6—7.

THE LANCET 'Vol 353' March 13, 1999   931

Levels Of Violence And Medication In A Special Prison Unit, 1986-1995.

Dr Bob Johnson, Consultant Psychiatrist,

introduction

Violent disruptive prisoners pose a sharp challenge to any prison system. Society locks violent citizens away, the prison service itself has fewer options. For, as one Home Secretary put it, "the mood and temper of the public with regard to the treatment of crime and criminals is one of the most unfailing tests of a country . . . [being the] sign and proof of the living virtue in it" [Winston Churchill 1910, Hansard].

Violence is an increasingly serious social disease. Murder is already the commonest cause of death in woman at work, and the second commonest for men in the USA [US Dept of Labour Report 1994 in Economist Dec. 3rd 1994, p 67]. It is set to rise inexorably in the UK, according to a recent monograph [Oliver James, "Violence against the person". Free Association Press 1995]. A great deal more is known about its origins than is generally supposed, as Oliver James [op cit.] makes clear.

In England in the early 1980's, an enlightened penal policy lead to three Special Units being established, whose principal objective was to remove especially disruptive prisoners from the general system, while obviating the need to condemn them to long periods of segregation or solitary confinement. The Special Unit at Parkhurst Prison was opened in December 1985, and provides the data presented here.

Barlinnie was a Special Unit established in Scotland in 1973. Professor David Cooke's analysis [Brit J Criminol, Spring 1989, 129-143] showed that the regime there reduced assaults from an expected 105 to 2. The Barlinnie Special Unit was closed in December 1994.

From July 1991 to present, every prisoner in the Parkhurst Special Unit who consented was seen on a weekly basis by the consultant psychiatrist (currently all of them). The approach deployed was to pursue and attempt to disentangle the long term effects of Child Abuse, essentially an extension of Post Traumatic Stress Disorder (PTSD), along similar lines to those pioneered by Alice Miller ["For your Own Good", Virago, 1980]

method

Research was regarded from the outset as an important component of these Special Units. Detailed records of inmates' ill-discipline were recorded on a monthly diary sheet. These form the basis for the data presented. Although "diary data" is inevitably incomplete and inaccurate, actual physical injuries, either of inmate or staff, are significant enough to attract notice and ensure greater accuracy in recording.

Medication records are less complete, only since late 1992 has the pharmacy kept dispensing data on computer. The 1990/91 figure is therefore an extrapolation from the prescribing patterns as recorded in June 1991; the 1992/3 data is based on the first six months of 1993; 1994/95 is an extrapolation of drugs dispensed to the end of January 1995. The 12 month periods run from July 1st in each year.

results

The numbers of inmates in the Special Unit throughout this period did not vary widely, usually in the range of 14 to 16, with a maximum of 18; a total of 54 men passing through in the 9 years. Currently there are 15, all lifers except one serving 16 years, and all for murder or attempted murder, except one for firearms offences.

The incidence of actual physical assault on another person is shown in table 1. Graph 1 groups this data into two year bands. Attacks on property are omitted. *Table 1 Assaults*

Medication levels are shown in kilograms of tranquillisers dispensed per annum. Drugs included are essentially those psychotropics in Chapter 4 of the BNF, omitting anti-depressants and analgesics as these are not commonly used to modify violent behaviour.

year	assaults
1986	17
1987	6
1988	5
1989	2
1990	5
1991	3
1992	3
1993	1
1994	0
1995	0

Year	Drugs in Kgs	costs
1990/91	3.5	£5500 est.
1991/92	no data	no data
1992/93	1.4	£3125
1993/94	1	£1050
1994/95	0.15	£254

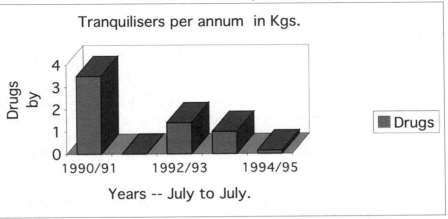

discussion

This data is interesting for two reasons in particular. Firstly though measurement of mental health is essentially subjective, happiness for instance being notoriously difficult to define, weighing the drugs dispensed in this relatively closed Special Unit (only 4 newcomers per annum on average) comes close to objectively measuring the subjective mental health of the inmates.

Secondly the conventional view that symptoms of violent disorders should be tackled by increasing medication has been stood on its head. Here a group of violent, unstable, ill-disciplined lifers have had their tranquillising medication consciously cut by 95%. This has not lead to an increase in violence. A reduction from 1 assault per inmate per annum in 1986, to zero in 1994 should do more than encourage the team currently working on the Unit. A reduction of around £5000 in sedative drug costs annually for 15 patients would, if applied nationally, represent savings of several million pounds.

It is clear that staff on the Special Unit are now adept at defusing violent incidents, and for the most part containing them within the Unit. They provide an indispensable supportive ethos which alone permits the weekly psychiatric therapy sessions to function. Sensitive areas could simply not even be discussed let alone explored without it.

Psychopaths are widely regarded as untreatable -- and clearly they commonly are, when the treatment offered is either unfocussed psychodynamic counselling, or sedative medication. The fantasies, symbolisms and "free association" favoured by Freud have little relevance to the harsh realism of maximum security prisoners -- indeed, on occasion, they can be counter-productive.

What Severe Personality Disorders require is a positive emotional involvement, together with a proactive approach to undoing the buried terror remaining from childhood trauma. This terror distorts thinking, and is therefore difficult to resolve unaided. It freezes the individual at the emotional age of five or thereabouts. By gently teasing out the implications, "Value Therapy" demonstrates that the original trauma is now over, and will not recur in adult life. Mature social strategies therefore become available, and violence is seen to be both socially maladaptive, and emotionally immature. The target is to eliminate it altogether, an aim shared by all participating inmates, who now, for the most part, co-operate with the Unit staff in reducing it.

Subjective clinical impressions are that most prisoners once over their initial shock, warmly welcome the opportunity to disentangle their childhood traumas, in the safe supportive atmosphere that this Special Unit currently provides. The results suggest the possibility of a method to reverse the rising tide of violence which besets society at large, and prisons in particular.

Bob Johnson   Monday, February 13, 1995   Consultant Psychiatrist,

Acknowledgements. I wish to thank Mike Christmas, Parkhurst Prison Principal Pharmacist, for his help with the computerised drug data; and of course the staff on C-Wing Special Unit without whose support this work could not have taken place.

Note : since the above was written, I gained access to the records for alarm bells actually rung on C-Wing from 1986 onwards. On average there were 20 a year – over the 10 year period a total of 200 would have been expected. However for the last three years there were none – giving a deficit of 60 alarm bells rung over the decade. Objective proof for those willing to look, that the approach adopted was successful. Even today, some 15 years later, I receive warm grateful letters from supposedly 'unfeeling psychopaths' – at least I do from those I have managed to regain contact with despite implacable official opposition.

The alarm bell data rather goes to show where the Home Office priorities are – not so much rehabilitation, as this clearly is, and the elimination of violence in prisons, which this approach manifestly achieved in the most challenging surroundings – but some other more pressing political or populist objective.

Evidence Prepared For The Joint Committee On The Draft Mental Health Bill
Session 2003-04, 16 September 2004
By Dr Bob Johnson   Consultant Psychiatrist

Preamble

1.   Psychiatry is currently in crisis. Having myself been trained in the early 1960s, when humane enlightened and above all optimistic teachers were available to me, I have seen my specialty lurch disastrously to the Right. Two books testify to this. The first is the DSM-IV (the Diagnostic and Statistical Manual of Mental Disorders 4th Edn. 1994), which derives from a Right Wing clique which took over the revision of the standard psychiatric text in 1980. The second is *Mad In America* by a Massachusetts journalist cataloguing with care and all too abundant evidence the disastrous indeed tragic black hole into which current psychiatric trends have landed us.

2.   If the Committee wishes to do more than scrape the surface of this vital topic, then it must, in my view, give due consideration to these two books – reading at the very least their prefaces. So vital do I consider *Mad In America* to be, in portraying a realistic and devastating indictment of our current practices that I would happily supply every member of the Committee with a copy, if so permitted.   The book's full details are – *Mad in America*: Bad Science, Bad Medicine, and the Enduring Mistreatment of the Mentally Ill'   by Robert Whitaker, Perseus, ISBN 0738203858 www.madinamerica.com

3.   The DSM-IV is more readily available since every psychiatric patient must now receive a codification from it.   Yet psychiatry based on the current DSM-IV is grievously flawed. Support for this view comes from an unimpeachable source – the preamble and introduction of the DSM-IV itself.   There we can read, on page xxiii, that *".. a diagnosis",* according to the DSM-IV, *"does not carry any necessary implications regarding the __causes__ of the individual's mental disorder."* [My emphasis]. No other branch of medicine would tolerate such a cavalier disregard of causative factors.   Without insight into causes, successful therapy is purblind – to revel in their absence in this way, borders on negligence.   In strictly medical terms, the DSM-IV is indefensible

4.   The human mind is the most fascinating item in the entire cosmos, yet the DSM-IV tries to bury it under a *'mind/body dualism'* which it dismisses as *"a reductionistic anachronism".* [page xxi] Such muddled thinking would fail even an elementary philosophy exam.   It certainly fails any practical exposure to psychiatric problems. No psychiatrist who listens attentively could arbitrarily exclude *"death of a loved*

one", as a potent cause of serious mental disease. The DSM-IV does just that on page xxi.

5.   The Committee may or may not be disposed to take the review of these matters to this depth. But I would assure the Committee that no great medical expertise is required to appreciate the issues involved – indeed the absence of a training in psychiatry could prove a positive benefit. In my own book, "*Emotional Health*", for instance, I criticise psychiatry based on the DSM-IV, for anathematising stress, emotions, the mind, and intent, thereby exposing us all to being mindless unfeeling robots. It's not hardware that fails, but software.

6.   **My Background** – I worked for 5 years as Consultant Psychiatrist in Parkhurst Prison in the Special Unit for those prisoners too violent for Broadmoor – today's DSPDs. I testified before the Fallon Inquiry at Ashworth Hospital being perhaps the only consultant with a clear workable definition of psychopathy, and solid experience of curing it – viz – while in Parkhurst Prison, no alarm bells were rung in C-Wing for 3 years, a unique record worldwide for any maximum security wing. Since 2000, I have prepared numerous Tribunal reports for long term patients in all three Maximum Security hospitals, and am seriously dismayed by what I observe to occur therein.

the Committees' Questions

7.   **1)   unambiguous basic principles? appropriate and desirable?**

7.1.   Currently established psychiatric principles may appear self-consistent and are often robustly and too successfully defended, as I have found. But, like all Right Wing strategies, the DSM-IV is based on a single slender fact, whose simplicity may at first appeal, but which inevitably unravels when exposed to complex human realities. The DSM-IV explicitly excludes human values, human aspirations, enlightened philosophies and above all, hope. It perpetrates a fraud on our psychiatric clientele. It is not too far fetched to call the result 'voodoo psychiatry'. After all, the benign and widely held notion that psychiatrists concern themselves with the childhood origins of mental disease is explicitly condemned and proscribed.

8.   **2)   definitions; conditions for treatment; provisions for Community assessment and treatment?**

8.1.   The prolific definitions provided in the DSM-IV are in practice, neither appropriate nor unambiguous. The string of symptoms which follows each 'diagnosis' is ill-defined, impractical in application, and with the exception of Post Traumatic Stress Disorder (PTSD), more confusing than helpful. Compulsion in therapy (which occurs in no other branch of medicine) touches on a serious contradiction in terms, which has been little thought through.

8.2.   The defining question here is why schizophrenics recover faster in non-Western cultures. This is the challenge which prompted Whitaker to write his book – see his preface.   Every psychiatrist should read this preface every year, and put in writing what they are going to do about it – everyone else should check that they do so.   Whitaker cites The Retreat in York (1796-1850), as providing more cures for psychoses than ever since. The Soteria Project by Loren Mosher confirms this.

9.   *3)   balance between human rights of the mentally ill, and safety?*

9.1.   This is always a difficult balance to achieve. It is posed every day in Cat A prisons. But there is false comfort to be had in supposing that the more draconian, the greater the security.   My work in Parkhurst Prison taught me that real security is 'dynamic security' i.e. security achieved by persuasion followed by consent. I would happily impose coercion when faced with, say, a mad axe man – but in the long term, self-confidence, self-esteem and emotional maturity are the only civilised safeguards available to a civilised society. And these must be inculcated in the offender from day one. My experience indicates that wisely and robustly applied, they suffice.

9.2.   The Draft Bill errs too heavily on compulsion, in my clear view, and not nearly enough on tailoring treatment to the individual such that they consent to it.

9.3.   Further, the Mental Health Review Tribunals I have participated in and observed first hand, often appear ill-equipped to support a judicious balance. Too many Tribunals set out to find reasons to err on the cautious side and to not-release.   Continuity of disease, as per Wintwerp, has too often been glossed over to further that end.   Legal precedents have been cited to me to the effect that where RMO and independent psychiatrist disagree, the Tribunal should favour the former – hardly encouraging of confidence in the system – since this is the only circumstance in which Tribunals matter at all.

9.4.   A particular case which might be of interest to the Committee is that of a 67 year old man with heart disease, who in a psychotic episode 34 years ago killed a girl. He improved with treatment in the early 1980s, such that a Tribunal in 1983 recommended his release. This was then vetoed by the Home Office, a practice dubious both clinically and judicially. Though no violence has occurred in the last 21 years, and despite his recent Tribunal agreeing that he was not currently 'abnormally aggressive nor seriously irresponsible', it was illogically concluded that he should remain in hospital to maintain this status quo – exactly the reverse, as I understand it, of the Wintwerp ruling.

10.   *4)   proposals necessary; workable, efficient, and clear? omissions?*

10.1.   Edward Fitzgerald QC during a lecture he gave to our small charity's annual conference asserted that this Bill was **unnecessary**.   I would happily email the relevant pages. He assured us that the Courts had abundant adequate legislation to cope with current problems. And when doctors usurp judicial functions, civilised society is compromised – something we are already perilously close to at times.

10.2. Judging by what I have seen of the current Mental Health Act in operation, even the present arrangements have serious, unaddressed flaws. Moreover, the new one is likely to impose catastrophic demands on currently available expertise to man the Tribunals, a problem even more acute in Scotland, as I gather.

10.3. The chief **omission** of course, is the emphasis on a more humane approach, predominant in the 1960s, as described above.

10.4. No one reading Whitaker as above, could then support compulsory treatment with today's psychoactive drugs – the side-effects are simply too dangerous.

11. **_5)_ _Is the institutional framework appropriate and sufficient for enforcement?_**

11.1. At a recent lecture, a prominent professor from Broadmoor assured us that though he would be happy to spend his proportion of the £270m allocated to DSPD units, he would be content to see the beds soon blocked, which he regarded as the end of the matter. He assured us that he had no notion of how to treat severe Personality Disorders. He was unaware of my work in Parkhurst Prison.

12. **_6)_ _safeguards? for example children? against misuse of ECT and psychosurgery?_**

12.1. Having prepared medico legal reports on a dozen individuals seriously damaged by ECT (I have a 14 min video confirming this), I have no confidence that this seriously invasive treatment will be adequately monitored. I would refer the Committee to the Texan Consent Form for ECT. I would also be happy to supply a copy of an Informed Consent Form which I drew up myself based on a more realistic assessment of the issues involved.

13. **_7) & 8)_ _no comment_**

14. **_9)_ _Is the Draft Mental Health Bill in full compliance with the Human Rights Act?_**

14.1. After almost half a century of clinical medicine, including a BA degree in psychology at Cambridge, there is no question in my mind that Human Rights are therapeutic. In other words, by assuring individuals that they matter, that their views will be taken into account, that in effect they themselves 'count' as individual citizens with rights and responsibilities – this approach increases self esteem, self-confidence, and thereby augments mental stability.

14.2.   The current draconian restrictions on some of my patients approach those of Kafka or the Gulag. If I might include one I am supporting at the moment, whose Tribunal comes up in November. He was convicted of Aggravated Bodily Harm after hitting a man coming drunk out of a pub. Sentenced to 6 years, he was due for release on 1 August 2004. On 30 July he was bundled off to Rampton, where his letters are opened and read, where his detention is now indefinite, and he has to cope with the burden of undue Home Office restrictions (s37). I have no confidence that his Tribunal will amend this situation. This is one of several in my current work load.

15.   *10) human and financial implications? effect on professionals? Analysis of effects, and costs?*

15.1.   I could wax voluble on these fascinating questions, but have already exceeded my wordage.

If I can assist further, I should be happy to do so – the offer with respect to Whitaker's book still stands.

Dr Bob Johnson**Consultant Psychiatrist,**   Saturday, 30 October 2004

☐   ☐   ☐   ☐

Web sites of interest

Robert Whitaker's website is www.MadinAmerica.com

Dr Peter Breggin's is www.Breggin.com

And the website for the International Center for the Study of Psychiatric and Psychology is www.icspp.org.

The website for The James Nayler Foundation, the charity I co-founded with my wife Sue, following the publicity given to my work by the BBC Panorama programme on 3 Match 1997 is www.TruthTrustConsent.com.

SELECTED READING LIST

The key book, as will be apparent is Robert Whitaker's
*Mad in America: Bad Science, Bad Medicine and the Enduring
Mistreatment of the Mentally Ill*   see www.MadinAmerica.com
Publisher: Perseus Books ISBN: 0738207993

Dr Peter Breggin has written extensively – two books stand out.

*Toxic Psychiatry: Why Therapy, Empathy and Love Must Replace
the Drugs, Electroshock and Biochemical Theories of the New
Psychiatry*   Peter Breggin, Dorothy Rowe (Introduction)
Publisher: Flamingo ISBN: 000637803X

And also –
*Talking Back to Ritalin: What Doctors Aren't Telling You About Stimulants and
ADHD* Publisher: Da Capo Press
ISBN: 0738205443   See www.Breggin.com

Dr Grace Jackson, mentioned in the text, has written
Rethinking Psychiatric Drugs : A Guide for Informed Consent
Publisher AuthorHouse   ISBN: 1420867423

My earlier book *Emotional Health* ISBN 0-991985-0-X, is
published by Trust Consent Publishing,
PO Box 49 Ventnor, Isle of Wight, PO38 9AA, UK.

I have not provided any detail of specific drug damage – these
books cover that more than adequately, and further, it is
manifestly not the absence of data, or of scientific evidence that
leaves us in our current psychiatric mire – it is denial on a
professional scale, a denial which must see the light of day
sooner rather than later. Given the level of support for it among
government departments and medical editors – help is needed
from all quarters to make that day soon.

⬛   ⬛   ⬛   ⬛